Ole Tales, Sweet Memories
My father and his unique stories from Sint Maarten

boek·scout

Eerste druk/First print © 2021 Maria Christina Plantz
and Charles Irving Plantz

Editors: Mary Jane Snow Helmund and Lynn Kaplanian Buller

ISBN: 978-94-643-1678-0

Publisher: Uitgeverij Boekscout Soest, the Netherlands
www.boekscout.nl

Maria Christina Plantz
and Charles Irving Plantz

OLE TALES,

SWEET MEMORIES

My father and his unique stories from Sint Maarten

Table of contents

INTRODUCTION TO 'OLE TALES, SWEET MEMORIES'

"What else did your father write?" The voice at the other end of the telephone line was gentle, soft spoken. It was Jos de Roo. He lives on Aruba but was temporarily in the Netherlands. He said that he made a great effort to find me. And now he had.

"Uh... he wrote a book about Taxation in the Netherlands Antilles, which is, or at least was, considered to be the handbook for taxadvisors..." This was the best answer I could give him. I don't really think it was an answer he expected. Quickly Jos started to explain that he would like to know more about my father. He asked if we could meet. We agreed to meet at my office in Amsterdam.

Although it is not unusual that people want to know more about my father or grandfather, my curiosity was peaked. Always proud to talk about this lovely man, whom I still miss a lot since he passed away in 1987, I was eager to hear the reason for his interest. So, I gathered some documentation and pictures for the meeting.

I met this friendly, white haired gentleman, at my office. He was clearly retired, but also clearly very active and doing something that invigorated him. He told me was doing research at Radio Nederland Wereldomroep for his doctoral (Ph.D) thesis. Radio Nederland Wereldomroep was a kind of Dutch BBC with, at one time, ambitions for worldwide broadcasting. Time was of the essence, because in the larger scheme of things this broadcasting institute, which existed since 1947, was faced with serious subsidy cuts in 2011. The archives would partially be destroyed if no good home could be found for them. He explained this had grave consequences for the integrity of its archives, which he needed access to for his research. Hence his haste. In his thesis he intended to set out the influence of Radio Nederland Wereldomroep on the development of literature of the Caribbean countries of the Dutch Kingdom. So far, so good, but I still did not see the relevance or connection with my father.

Then came the big surprise. He told me that whilst foraging in the dungeons of the archives of Radio Nederland Wereldomroep, he found a hidden treasure. Something he was not looking for nor had expected to find... Eighteen stories, written by my father between 1949 and 1952 in Sint Maarten English. Stories that he had read to the microphones of Radio Nederland Wereldomroep for broadcasting to the Windward Islands.

Jos de Roo went on to tell me that there were also stories by other Dutch Antillean and Surinamese writers. Many of them became well known writers. Some of them even are acknowledged as great contributors to the landscape of Dutch literature. So, he wondered whether my father had published anything worth studying.

"Well, he has, but only if you are interested in taxation."

He handed me photocopies of typescript pages, where here and there I could see the additions and deletions made in my father's handwriting. A quick scan of the texts reminded me of the five or six stories my father dictated to me during the last weeks of his life. Jumbie stories, all placed in Sint Maarten. These stories were given to Lio Capriles in Curaçao with the aim of publishing them with proceeds going to the cancer foundation. Unfortunately, this never happened.

This was an exciting and pleasant encounter. I told Jos de Roo about my father and showed him the selected pictures. We agreed to meet again and that he would keep me informed of the progress he was making with his thesis. It stayed with me all day, the happy feeling.

I had no clue my father had done this.

I asked my brother and sisters. Neither did they. All of a sudden, the two or three little pictures in the photo album my mother used to have made sense. They showed my father, probably in his early twenties, sporting a dandy moustache, talking into a microphone. Some of these pictures are lost. We looked. But I can still see them in my minds eye.

I asked my mom what she knew about this. She remembered that my father would go to Hilversum about once a month to read the story he had written that month. He got paid well according to her. Twelve and a half guilders, a fortune… and a welcome addition to his monthly study allowance. Enough for the train tickets to Hilversum and back, to take her out for a rice table at Indonesian Restaurant 'Tante Lien', and some money to spare. She also remembered that when he ran out of stories, he decided to make some up to continue. It made me curious.

Studio Radio Nederland Wereld Omroep, 1952
Collection Ellie Plantz

Was there more that I didn't know? I decided to Google. My father may not have been of the internet age, but we have been surprised by other internet finds before. And I actually found something. One reference provided me with a link to a secured mp3 fragment. A recording dating back to May 20, 1950 of one of his stories. 'Ole Capin Johnson'.

I couldn't believe what I was hearing - a younger version of my father's voice. I have been able to share this sound fragment with some who knew him well and they have all enjoyed hearing his voice again. Sweet memories, worth sharing. Unfortunately the link is no longer active, but I made a simple copy and listen to it often and always with a smile on my face.

Irving Plantz 1947,
Collection Ellie Plantz

THE REMARKABLE STORIES OF IRVING PLANTZ

- By Dr. B. Jos de Roo -

One of the most surprising finds, when researching the signifi-cance of Radio Nederland Wereldomroep for the development of the Dutch Antillean and Surinamese literature in the forties and fifties, was the discovery of the 'Bovenwindse Vertellingen' (Tales of the Windward Islands) of Irving Plantz. Between the 19th of February 1949 and the 8th of November 1952, he told 22 stories about Sint Maarten, of which 17 have been preserved. It is quite possible that he started telling stories earlier, because the radio scripts for the period between August 3, 1947 and February 19, 1949 were missing from the archives. From the very start of the West Indian broadcast, J. Van der Walle, who was the head of the West Indian department, paid a lot of attention to recording oral literature of the Dutch Antilles and Surinam. Raúl Römer did this in Papiamento with the Curaçaolenean 'Cuentanan di Nanzi', Johan Ferrier in Sra-nan Tongo with the Surinamese 'Anansitoris' and Irving Plantz with his tales of the Windward Islands in what was said to be "dat sappige Bovenwindse Engels" ("that juicy Windward Islands English"), as the broadcaster announced it. The 63 recorded stories thus became one of the largest collections' oral narratives of the

Dutch Caribbean. It was not in line with common convention in the forties and fifties to have the treasure of oral tales recorded by natives of the colonies in the local language for literary reasons. Until then foreigners had done this; not for esthetical reasons, but more based on anthropological and linguistic curiosity.

It is noteworthy that Plantz does not tell any spider stories. With this he confirms what the sparse secondary literature states about the oral tradition of the Windward Islands: these stories were not original to Sint Maarten, but that they do occur on Sint Eustatius. According to Droog the Nanzi tales can be found on former the Netherlands Antilles where Papiamento is spoken as well as on Sint Eustatius.[i] Sypkens Smit, who conducted research on Sint Maarten culture between 1979 and 1981, states that the animal stories from African origin that are told on Sint Maarten feature Bó Monkey an Bó Lion. According to him other animal stories are imported through books. (217/218). It is possible that Plantz also told stories with these protagonists, as not all of his contributions may have been preserved and it is likely that he also contributed to the broadcasts before the 19th of February 1949.

Plantz is the first Sint-Maartener who published oral literature and he thereby compiled the largest collection until then. Rutgers claims that Parsons' collection of stories, proverbs and riddles of 1936 is the oldest collection. She published 16 stories from 8 informants. It was not until 1981 that Sypkens Smit was the next to publish those stories. He provides three stories that were recorded by Camille Baly. The significance of the oral literature by Plantz is therefore important, because recording thereof seems to have been a step-child on Sint Maarten in a time that the interest to record oral tradition arose.

Plantz tells three kinds of stories. Firstly, stories with a prominent role for phantasy with probably no historical origin. Stories with animals and trees that speak to people or each other. This is the case with 'Damfool and sensible', 'The sensiblest man in the world', 'The three lill pigs' and 'Mongoose sorrow'. Twice it occurs that a fisherman returns a little fish to the sea after being caught, because it promises to fulfill a wish: in 'Capin Johnson and the lil red snapper' Johnson will always catch more than enough fish and in 'The Black Rocks and magic fish' Granville can always return to make a new wish. Plantz wanted to preserve these stories for posterity, because the tradition of passing on of this treasure of tales was quickly dying out.

In the tradition of this kind of stories Plantz sometimes mentions the origin at the start. He begins the story about 'Damfool and Sensible' as follows: "*A gon tell you a story Granmother tole me when a was a lil boy.*" This also happens at the start of his next story, 'The sensiblest man in the world', which he mentions is a story he was told when he was young: "*Wen a was a lil boy a use to like to hear stories, an a suppose all lil children like to hear them. Evry coutry got it own fairy tales and asuppose lots of these are made by the fathers but especially by the mothers just to keep dey children quiet. The last time a told you the story about how Damfool cook he mother, an today a got another old story to tell you. Tis funny butmost a the stories you hear when you young are about talking animals or trees or about foolish and sensible people an most a the stories are cruel and the children seem to like them this way.*"

Secondly Plantz tells stories about legendary people from the past. They often live on in the collective memory of small oral communities in the stories that are passed on. Because of the great attention that the Kompa Nanzi stories got, such stories have been neglected in the studies about Caribbean oral history. It is to Plantz' merit that he did not do that whilst recording the Sint Maarten oral stories. Probably Ole Captain Johnson, who figures in two of the stories, was one of these Sint Maarten legendary figures. It is easy to establish that Ole Johannes actually existed. He is the lead protagonist in the stories 'Ole Johannes and the cotton thieves' and 'Simple island justice' and a supporting figure in 'Jim and Anna', where he gives his loyal servant a piece of land. At the end of the story 'Simple island justice' the escaped thief Mooner Joseph mentions the last name of Ole Johannes. He says: "*A goin right back in Mr. Romondt cane piece.*" From this one can trace back who Ole Johannes must have been. In 'For the love of St. Maarten' Will Johnson dedicates two chapters to the family Van Romondt. He gives an overview of all of the family members who lived on Sint Maarten. Two family members bear the name Johannes. The first is Diederik Johannes, the forefather of the Sint Maarten Van Romondts. He was born in 1781 in Holland. In 1801 or 1803 he came to Sint Maarten. From 1820 to 1840 he was the governor. The other Johannes is his eldest son Johannes Willem (1805-1849). He was governor from 1840 to 1849. Probably the story is about him because Ole Jo is not depicted in the stories as someone who came from outside the island. In any case it is clear that what happens in the stories dates back to the first half of the nineteenth century.

It is also certain that Ole Jo played a role in the collective oral tradition. This can be seen at the start of the story of the March 17, 1951 broadcast: 'Simple island justice'. Plantz starts with: *"Hello Folks, to nite a gon tell you a story some body from home wrote me about, an a hope he is listenin to night."* Probably the writer of the letter from Sint Maarten did not send him this story, because I assume he would have mentioned that. The letter seems to have been a reaction to a earlier story by Plantz about the same protagonist Ole Johannes. This story was broadcast on February 11, 1950 and talks about how Ole Johannes finally caught the cotton thieves. 'Simple island justice' also relates about a thief, but this thief in the end pulled a fast one on Ole Johannes. It is quite possible that the writer of the letter reminded Plantz of the story where Ole Johannes had a taste of defeat and that Plantz then decided to tell the story again. The letter Plantz referred to proves that there were more than one story circulating on Sint Maarten featuring Ole Jo.

In the third category of stories Plantz most of all wants to paint a picture of olden times and describe what every day looked like. 'Blessed rain, cursed rain' relates the dire consequences of a long drought and the sudden abundant rainfall afterwards. Rogue goats and the nuisance they cause feature in 'Jim and Anna' and 'Damn goats'. In 'Sharks in Lamejo' Plantz talks about what they used to do in olden times when a school of sharks would come into Baie de L'Embouchure. 'Smuggling trick', is a story about contraband where a diligent policeman is tricked. He smells that there should be rum in a cask and when he actually knocks the cask over it appears that the cask is full of cow dung, because the smugglers just sprinkled a bit of rum on the cask. The story shows that the sympathy of the people was biased to the smugglers. In 'Hurricane!' Plantz relates what happens when a hurricane rages over the island.

According to Maria van der Sluijs-Plantz, his daughter, her father was devoted to recording life as it was in Sint Maarten because he saw Sint Maarten change from an agricultural community to a migration community where the men left to work in the oil refineries of Aruba and Curacao or for the sugar campaign to Cuba. He wanted to record the agricultural community in stories. A number of these old daily life stories hardly have a plot. For him it was important to relate what the people did when sharks came into Baie L'Embouchure. He personalizes the stories for his audience by telling it from the perspective of two boys who experience this event. It is clear that these two boys are made up and are not part of the oral tradition of Sint Maarten. But they are not the main theme of the story. The main purpose was to record the experience as related by people who had actually lived through such an event. This experience is part of the collective memory of people about days gone by. This is what Plantz passes on in his oral literature.

The stories for the Wereldomroep are not to only place where one can find Irving Plantz great fascination for the customs and usages of old Sint Maarten. He was an important source on these matters for Jean Glasscock, author of 'The Making of an Island - Sint Maarten Saint Martin'. Plantz relates in this book about, among others, Van der Zee, governor from 1920-1923 and a fanatical crusader against the practice of contraband between the French and Dutch side of the island. Van der Zee had the practice to have women, who were caught smuggling, shorn bald. According to the story that Plantz had heard from his father Van der Zee got a taste of his own medicine: "*Van der Zee was set upon by some women who held onto him and gave him a beating. He swore they were men dressed as women, but in any event, he got his licks.*" (90) He further relates about the past practice of the 'jollifications', a custom where neighbours would come en masse to help with planting or clearing of the land (143/144), about the origin of the name 'Man of War Shoals' (157/158) and the early custom of help at the birth of a child. (116/117)

Irving Plantz was the oral story telling pioneer of Sint Maarten. His stories show clearly that Sint Maarten had its very own oral tradition. The idiosyncrasy of these stories is that actual legendary island people and customs played an important role. This goes to show that the origin of oral tradition is in fact far more recent than has so far been documented.

Literature:
Aart G. Broek, *De kleur van mijn eiland.* Leiden, 2006.
J. Droog, *Biba Nanzi!* Aruba, z.j. [=1969].
Jean Glasscock, *The Making of an Island.* Z.p., 1985.
Will Johnson, *For the Love of St.Maarten.* New York, 1987.
B. Jos de Roo, *Praatjes voor de West.* Z.p., 2014.
Wim Rutgers, *Schrijven is zilver, spreken is goud.* Z.p., 1994.
M.P. Sypkens Smit, *Beyond the Tourist Trap.* Amsterdam, 1995.

CHARLES IRVING PLANTZ – A HUMBLE MAN

So now that I have decided, with the approval of my brother and sisters, to share the 'Ole tales', I want to introduce you to my father. Or better, to my father as a young man.

He led a full life and there is much more to tell about him. But I am not writing his full biography. I will just describe those elements of his life which defined him, before he wrote the stories.

He was strongly defined by his Caribbean heritage and family ancestry. He was also very much defined by that lonesome and terrifying experience of living through and surviving World War II, far away from home.

Those who knew him will agree. The man he ultimately became was modest, renowned for his values, standards of integrity, intellectual prowess. He was very demanding of himself and the people around him, always in pursuit of making things better. The concept of 'we' definitely had a priority over the concept of 'me', where 'me' was only justified or even relevant if acting in service of 'we'. This was evidenced in his community service. He served years on the board of the Monseigneur Verriet Instituut, a home for severely handicapped children on Curaçao. He was a strong supporter of the labour unions, offering free legal advice and strategic support during negotiations. He volunteered his free time often and long on many fundraising community projects for the Kiwanis. Without ever expecting anything in return, he had a spirit of generosity which nowadays may be considered old fashioned, but is sincerely missed. He was a quiet, self-effacing, caring man.

He 'walked the talk' and expected others to do the same. He was strict but fair. But most of all in his humility he was very approachable, regardless of his standing in the community, always ready to extend a helping hand and to do the right things right. He was a role model for many.

My father was a silent man, soft spoken. But when he had something to say, people stopped and listened. And now, after so many years, the stories he wrote as a student in his mid twenties have been found. The stories in which he ruminates about Sint Maarten life as he remembered it... Sint Maarten lore... all with a touch of nostalgia. These are the stories we share with you in this book.

FAMILY HISTORY

Who was Charles Irving Plantz?

Like many West Indian people, my father was connected with more islands in the Caribbean than only Sint Maarten. Through family ties, the mighty Beauperthuy 'tribe' into which he was born, and through the different official postings to other islands which his father pursued in his career (as tax receiver, acting notary, acting lieutenant governor, public servant and politician), my father was connected to at least Saint Thomas, Sint Eustatius, Martinique, Les Saints, Guadeloupe, Sint Maarten/Saint Martin, Bonaire, Aruba, Curaçao and all the French Caribbean islands where the Beauperthuy tribe had spread.

It is this very diverse lineage of my father's ancestors and their involvement with historical events of Saint Martin/Sint Maarten that defined him. This ancestry formed the foundation for a demanding family legacy, to which he was expected to live up, combined with the strong old-fashioned values of respect for all and service in humility, which both his parents practiced in all they did until the day they died.

Another episode in his life that most certainly defined him was the period of World War II. The experience of living through that nightmare, far away from home and surviving as a young brown-skinned man is a story in its own right.

Some exploration into these family roots and the war experience will give insight and provide colour and nuance to those who did not know him, for a better understanding of this humble and silent man was, who wrote the 'Ole tales'.

FAMILY TREE

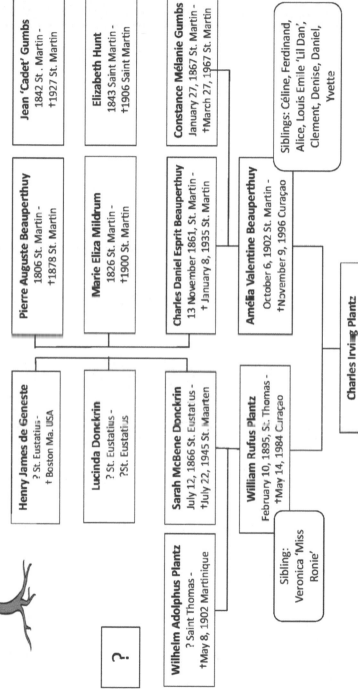

THE ROOTS FROM FATHER'S SIDE

Irving's father, William Rufus Plantz, was born on Saint Thomas on February 10, 1895[ii]. As the island was under Danish rule, he became Danish by birth.

My Great Grandmother
Sarah Macbene Donckrin

My great-grandmother (my father's grandmother) from father' side was named Sarah. She was born on Sint Eustatius on July 12, 1866[iii] in 'The Village'. Sarah's mother, Irving's greatgrandmother, was Lucinda Donckrin, who had been a slave. Sarah's father, Irving's great grandfather, was Henry Geneste (also referred to as Henry de Geneste). He was the owner of Lucinda. Sarah is said to have been raised at the home of Mr. Geneste. Her name was recorded in many different ways: Sarah MacBene, Sarah MacBene Donckrin, Sarah Geneste, Sarah MacBean de Geneste and Sarah Penya.

There is also a record where she is mentioned as Mary Sarah de Geneste.[iv]

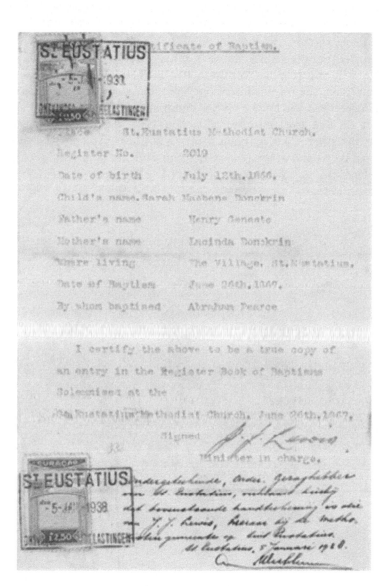

Certificate of Baptism.

St.Eustatius Methodist Church.

Register No.   3019

Date of birth   July 12th.1866.

Child's name. Sarah Mashena Donckrin

Father's name   Henry Geneste

Mother's name   Lucinda Donckrin

Where living   The Village, St.Eustatius.

Date of Baptism   June 26th,1867.

By whom baptised   Abraham Pearce

I certify the above to be a true copy of an entry in the Register Book of Baptisms Solemnised at the St.Eustatius Methodist Church, June 26th,1867.

Signed

Minister in charge.

Document from collection W.R. Plantz estate

From statements made by Sarah in a notarial deed in 1938 we learn that between 1895, the year William Rufus Plantz was born, and 1902, the year her common law husband William Adolphus Plantz died, she travelled between Saint Thomas and Saint Eustatius. After 1902 she lived with her children, William Rufus and Veronica on Sint Eustatius. She moved to Sint Maarten in 1924, the year my father, Charles Irving Plantz was born. Except for a short period when she accompanied her son and his family to Bonaire, she lived on Sint Maarten at the Belvédère Estate until she died on July 22, 1945.

Herman Wilhelm , Sarah MGeneste and Charles Irving Plantz, around 1935.
Collection W.R. Plantz

My Great Grandfather
William Adolphus Plantz

My great-grandfather (my father's Danish grandfather from father' side), was recorded to be a William Adolphus Plantz. He was not married to Sarah. He died tragically in 1902 as result of the eruption of the volcano Mont Pelée, near the village of Saint Pierre on Martinique. The pyroclastic surge[v] which came down and completely covered the town of Saint Pierre also scuttled the CS Grappler, on which his Irving's grandfather had been working.

The Grappler, a cable repair ship of the West India and Panama Telegraph Company[vi], was lost with its entire crew on May 8, 1902 as result of this disaster. This loss was heavily mourned on Saint Thomas. The *Saint Thomæ Tidende* of May 10th, 1902 published the tragedy together with a crew list which shows the name of "W. Wilhelm, alias Plantz – able seaman and blacksmith" as one of the crewmembers. I found the text of this article on the internet:

The Loss of the
Grappler & the List of the Victims
(St. Thomæ Tidende, 10 May 1902)

It is with the most profound regret that we record the loss of the cable steamer Grappler and her whole complement of fifty-three souls. The deplorable calamity occurred at Martinique and is due, as already known, to the volcanic eruption there. So far, only the bare, heartbreaking reality of the ship's loss has come to hand and that not one remains to tell the tale! The terrible nature of the catastrophe at Martinique, which makes the stoutest and coldest heart and aghast, staggered us all in its horror and elicited our deepest regrets. But the lamentable wreck of the familiar Grappler has touched us in a sense more keenly. From her worthy captain right down to the humblest in her gallant crew all were, by birth or otherwise, connected with St. Thomas, therefore the disaster can for us be regarded as a domestic calamity, and as such it has naturally called forth the deepest sympathy of friends, acquaintances, all. To the families, widows, and other relatives so overwhelmed with grief at their sudden bereave-

ment, we most sincerely tender our heartfelt condolence in their terrible affliction. In token of respect, flags were put at half-mast in town and in the harbour.

The following comprise the officers and crew of the ill-fated Grappler:
OFFICERS......
CREW......
W. WILHELM, alias PLANTZ, Able Seaman and Blacksmith.

http://www.rootsweb.ancestry.com/~vicgl/MontPeleeEruption.pdf

CS Grappler
Owner West India and Panama Telegraph Company
Built in 1880 by J. Laing and Company, Sunderland
Length 208.5 ft., Breadth 29.3 ft, Depth 16.2 ft. Gross tonnage 868
Lost on May 8th, 1902 in the harbor of Saint Pierre, Martinique, together with 17 other vessels when the Mont Pelée erupted.

The *Saint Thomæ Tidende* of May 28, 1902 published a poem by Samuel Industrious of St. Thomas in honor of this event and those affected by it. [vii]

My Grandfather
William Rufus Plantz

Collection W.R. Plantz Estate

Irving's father, my grandfather, son of Sarah de Geneste and Wilhelm or William Adolphus Plantz was called William Rufus Plantz. He was born on Saint Thomas on February 10th, 1895 and grew up on Saint Eustatius. He apparently was a very clever boy and was soon singled out by his teachers for extracurricular training in accounting and other academic topics. The schooling possibilities were limited on Saint Eustatius. But his training continued after he had completed all available classes whilst also holding a paid position as lighthouse keeper. His duty entailed making sure that the lighthouse was lit on time at night and switched off on time in the morning. When a position became available at the office of the tax receiver on Sint Maarten, his teachers recommended him for the job.

He then moved to Sint Maarten. He was a self-made man who studied his entire life, ordering law books and books on taxation to feed his thirst for knowledge. He was also active as acting notary on Sint Maarten before being stationed on other Dutch Caribbean islands.

He made many friends on Sint Maarten, and was somewhat of a Dandy.

Back row Malcolm 'Malley' Wathey, Willem de Weever and Rufus Plantz. Front row: Fred Conner, Fred Labega and Harry Wathey brother of Malley Wathey. Some of the old St. Martin well known family names.
Collection Yvette Fleming-Hodge

Because of his friendship with Ferdinand Beauperthuy, the son of the mayor of the French side, he came in touch with Amélia Valentine Beauperthuy, whom he married in July 1923.

As government official he served on many islands of the former Netherlands Antilles and went into politics in 1937 to participate in the first Staten (Senate) elections. After being elected he moved to Curaçao, where he held office in various important functions - amongst others, as Chairman of the Staten and Cabinet Minister.

As Cabinet Minister he played an important role after the Second World War as negotiator with the Netherlands over the islands' autonomy. This negotiation led to the Kingdom Charter of 1954 and relative autonomy of the Netherlands Antilles.[viii]

In 1948 he was also one of the founders of the 'Nationale Volks Partij' or 'NVP', together with Dr. Moises Frumencio Da Costa Gomez. This political party still exists but now is known as 'Partido National di Pueblo' or 'PNP'.

He retired on Curacao, where he died in 1987. He was buried in Sint Maarten.

THE ROOTS FROM MOTHER'S SIDE

Irving's mother, my grandmother Amélia Valentine Gumbs was born on Chambard Hill in French Quarter on October 6, 1902 on the French side of Saint Martin. She was a French national by birth.

My Great Grandmother
Mélanie Constance Gumbs

Valentine's mother was Mélanie Constance Gumbs (1866 – 1967). In official records her profession is recorded as seamstress. But she was most famous for the little grocery shop and bakery she ran from her house on Chambard Hill, across from where the Saint Joseph church is now located in French Quarter. She baked not only bread, but a wide array of cakes and all kind of confectionary using her outside wood-fired oven. Mélanie comes from the Gumbs lineage, which is a 'tribe' in itself.

Mélanie Gumbs, was not married with Charles Daniel Esprit Beauperthuy 'Mister Dan' when Valentine was born. This common law union led to a further extension of the Gumbs family lineage into the Beauperthuy family. Mélanie was known as a good, God fearing woman who was always ready to help anyone in need.

Valentine was the fourth child of Melanie and Mister Dan and had 7 siblings, Céline, Ferdinand and Alice who were born before her, and Louis Emile (Lil' Dan), Denise, Daniel and Yvette Alexina who were all born after her.

The only picture we have of Mélanie, 'Mister Dan' and most of their children. Picture probably taken in 2016 when the baby Yvette Alexina was born in March. From left to right: 'Mister Dan', Alice, Denise, Mélanie, (baby) Yvette, Ferdinand (back), Daniel (front), Valentine, Louis Emile 'Lil Dan' front, unknown, unknown. Missing on the picture is Céline.
Collection Ferdie Beauperthuy and Karine Fleming

My Great Grandfather
Charles Daniel Esprit Beauperthuy –
'Mister Dan'

Valentine's father, Charles Daniel Esprit Beauperthuy (1861 – 1935), was a judge and served as maire (French mayor) of Saint Martin from 1904 to 1919. He was decorated with the Legion D'Honneur. He was a goodlooking and well-respected man on both sides of the island. It is said of him that he started the mulatto strain of Beauperthuy descendants in Saint Martin/Sint Maarten in the village of French Quarter.

The Beauperthuy family was one of the early arrivals from France in the French Caribbean. The family originated from the Perigord area of France and were an accomplished lot, hailed to be doctors, pharmacists and engineers. The first arrival in the French Caribbean is recorded to have been in 1771, when Pierre Beauperthuy, was appointed by the king of France to provide medical care at the military hospital in Guadeloupe.

Charles Daniel Esprit Beauperthuy 'Mister Dan'
Collection Yvette Fleming-Hodge

From there the Beauperthuy's spread over the Caribbean, the Americas and the rest of the world.

In 1846 the Beauperthuy family obtained the concession for salt winning of the Orleans salt pond. With their background as engineers, they built the Quartier D'Orleans Salt Pond and have assisted with the building of the Philipsburg Great Salt Pond. The family was very much involved with the community of Saint Martin and many members have played active roles as judge, maire and senator.

Whilst it is a well known 'secret' that Mister Dan fathered many children with other women than Mélanie Gumbs, hers were the children he ever formally acknowledged (in 1929), and eventually 'legitimized' by marriage to Mélanie just before he died in 1935. His legitimate heirs were then Valentine and most of her siblings.

Although this singled Valentine and her 'legitimized' siblings out from the other offspring, they all lived well together and respected each other as family, referring to them as half-brothers or half-sisters, but definitely part of the Beauperthuy 'tribe'. This sense of the wider family circle was passed on to my father who loved the extended family and knew each and every one of them. He passed on this love for the extended family to us, his children.

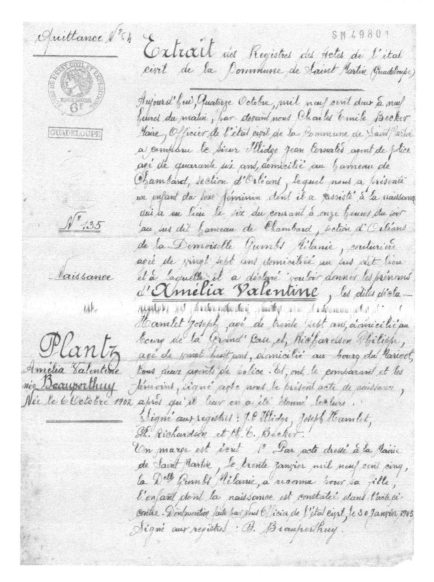

Extract from the Civil Registry confirming name change from Amélia Valentine Gumbs to Amélia Valentine Beauperthuy . Collection W.R. Plantz estate

2° Par acte en date du vingt cinq juillet, mil neuf cent vingt trois, dressé à la Mairie de Saint Martin, la D°lle Gumbs Amélia Valentine, dont la naissance est constatée dans l'acte ci-contre, a contracté mariage avec le sieur Plantz William Rufus.

Dont mention faite par Vous, Officier de l'état civil, le 25 juillet 1923.

Signé aux registres : Ferdinand Morales.

3° Par Acte dressé à la Mairie de Saint Martin, le vingt quatre Avril mil neuf cent vingt neuf, le sieur Beauperthuy Charles Daniel Esprit, a reconnu pour sa fille l'enfant dont la naissance est constatée dans l'acte ci-contre.

Dont mention faite par Vous, Officier de l'état civil, le 24 Avril 1929.

Signé aux registres : S. C. Fléming.

4° Par leur mariage célébré à la Mairie de Saint Martin le six Janvier mil neuf cent trente cinq, le sieur Beauperthuy Charles Daniel Esprit et la D°lle Gumbs Constance Mélanie, ont légitimé l'enfant, dont la naissance est constatée dans l'acte ci-contre.

Dont mention, faite par Vous, Officier de l'état civil, le 6 Janvier 1935.

Signé aux registres : S. C. Fléming.

Expédition Collationnée.

Saint Martin, le premier Mai, mil neuf cent trente sept.

Le Maire, Officier de l'État civil.

My Grandmother
Amélia Valentine Beauperthuy

Collection Yvette Fleming-Hodge

Irving's mother (my grandmother), the daughter of Constance Mélanie Gumbs and Charles Daniel Esprit Beauperthuy 'Mister Dan' was called Amélia Valentine Beauperthuy. She was affectionately known as 'Miss Valen'. She was born on Saint Martin on October 6th, 1902 and grew up in French Quarter.

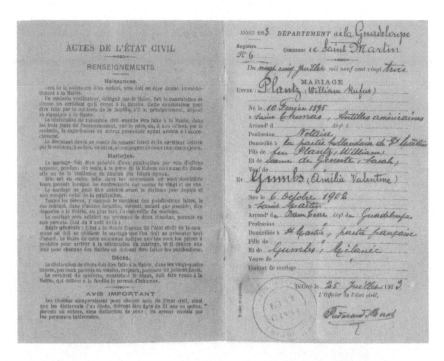

She was introduced to my grandfather by her brother Ferdinand. My great-aunt Yvette told me that my grandmother was playing hard to get in her own way. My grandfather had to convince her to see him by picking her up one Sunday for church with a horse-drawn carriage. They eventually got married on July 25th, 1923.

My grandmother oversaw the Belvédère Estate which raised goats and cattle whenever she was on Sint Maarten. Due to the appointment of her husband as government official on other islands of the former Netherlands Antilles, she followed her husband and the family eventually settled on Curaçao.

Her life was not easy because of the wandering eye of my grandfather and his many not so secret amorous liaisons. She sometimes seemed bitter. But she always stuck to her family values.

She was a beautiful woman, with light green-grey eyes, very loved and respected within the family and the community at large.

She was a very demanding and strict grandmother. She was a generous grandmother if you were one of her 'favourites'. If you were not you did not merit her attention.

She was a great cook and hostess and was always ready to help anyone. She died on Curaçao in November 1995 and was buried on Sint Maarten.

Herman 'Manchi', Valentine and Irving, Sint Maarten 1932
Collection Yvette Plantz

GROWING UP ON THE ISLANDS (1924 – 1938)

Charles Irving Plantz was born on Belvédère Estate, Upper Princess Quarters on the island of Sint Maarten on May 7th, 1924, as the first son of William Rufus Plantz and Amélia Valentine Plantz-Beauperthuy. William Rufus had purchased the estate a year earlier.

Irving's aunt Yvette, lovingly referred to by many as M'am Fleming, was eight years old when he was born. She remembered the occasion vividly. Both she and her sister Denise were living on the Belvédère Estate with their sister Valentine, to go to the Saint Joseph School in Philipsburg. She told me how after the baby was born, she was brought in to see her sister and the baby. She remembered she was crying but did not remember why. She did remember that the midwife said to her: *"Don cry child, the box open easy"*, leaving her to wonder what 'the box' was.

Irving spent his childhood growing up on different islands of what were then Dutch colonies due to the many different functions his father took on during his career. From 1924 to 1928 his father, William Rufus Plantz was Receiver and acting Lieutenant Governor of Bonaire. Irving lived in Bonaire as an infant from 1925 until sometime in 1927[ix] when he travelled back to Sint Maarten with his mother, his grandmother Sarah and his aunt Veronica or 'Miss Ronie' as she was affectionately known. Valentine was pregnant with her second child, Herman Wilhelm, who was born on Sint Maarten on October 29, 1927.

In 1928 Irving travelled with his mother and brother to Aruba. His father had been appointed there as Government Tax Receiver. This must have been an important position, as at some point in time three houses were built on the Klip. One for the Lieutenant Governor, one for the Judge and one for the Government Receiver. Irving went to school on Aruba.

In 1931 his aunt Yvette and aunt Alice joined the family in Aruba. At this time there were grave concerns for his health due to illness characterized by raging fevers. The concern was so serious that a businessman, in a letter addressed to his father, expressed his sympathy for the sick child.

During this time in Aruba great friendships were forged with the Ecury family, of which Aura Ecury remained a close friend of Valentine for life. The family lived in Aruba until at least December 1932. They were all in Sint Maarten when Irving's uncle Daniel Beauperthuy married Mathurine Bryan.

They must have stayed on a while in Sint Maarten and lived on Belvédère Estate. Irving and Herman, or Manchi as he was called, went to the sini josephser hurd to Phillipsburg, first by foot, then by horse and eventually by bicycle. Although few facts are known about this period, a childhood friendship was made with Louis Richardson that lasted his whole life. They shared a passion for cricket. Irving loved to fish and hunt ground doves and many were the family members who would take him along. This love of wandering through nature, sitting by the seaside and being at peace with the universe stayed with him for the rest of his life.

When Irving's father assumed a new function in Curaçao at the Receivers Office, they travelled to Curaçao to join him in January 1933. There they lived at Penstraat 44. Mabel, a maid who lived with Valentine on Belvédère joined them. In April the family was again joined by his aunt Yvette.

They stayed in Curaçao until January 1934 when William Rufus Plantz was granted a year off with paid leave for travel abroad with his family to New York[x], after having served as public official for seventeen years.[xi]

The family was reunited in Sint Maarten in January 1935 when they were all present at the funeral of Valentine's father. Whilst William Rufus then traveled back and forth to Curacao for political reasons, the family remained on Sint Maarten until early 1938.

In 1937 William Rufus was a contender in the first election for representation of the Windward Islands in the Staten (senate) on Curaçao. This is where the center of government of the Dutch Caribbean islands was located at the time. This election was a hot topic on the islands as the validity of my grandfather's candidacy on the ballot was disputed by 'Broertje Brouwer', the editor of the periodical 'Slag om slag'. Mr. Brouwer claimed that the electoral lists were incomplete and structured in such a way to ensure the election of William Rufus Plantz as preferred candidate of the colonial establishment in Curaçao.

According to Will Johnson: the 'Amigoe', a Roman Catholic newspaper on Curaçao in no uncertain terms favoured the election of Plantz over Brouwer, as the latter was looked upon as a radical.' [xii]

The question of validity focused on whether or not William Rufus' last name was in fact 'Plantz' and Brouwer even claimed that my grandfather was German. As the records in those days were not perfect there was a lot of concern with the supporters of William Rufus whether enough objective proof could be gathered to counter the assertions of Brouwer that the name and nationality were incorrect.

This led to a search for people, both on Sint Eustatius and on Saint Thomas, who could confirm the parentage of William Rufus. These people were asked to give a statement before notary public of what they knew about his parents. Whilst these notarial declarations confirmed his father to be William A. Plantz of Saint Thomas, the certificate of baptisim which was obtained from the All Saints Church in Saint Thomas in 1933, was the only original official document confirming the name of his father.

Ernest Voges in front of Statia Government building
Photo by Willem Polman courtesy of Will Johnson

Mr. Voges, a government official on Saint Eustatius at the time, who had been instrumental in obtaining some of these notarial declarations and documents always confirmed his support to William Rufus in the upcoming elections.

Voges wrote:

"St Eustatius, August 20, 1937
Dear Plantz;
Got your letter o.k. I am sorry but I cannot find the certificate for you. I am enclosing a baptisim certificate I got from the Methodist church. Your mother's name does not appear in the registers. I went over those pages one for one.
It appears that someone wants to make bad feeling among the gang of us. The old man wrote me that someone wrote him that I was not doing my best over here, as I feel that I should have been running for representative. Now you

quite know that I have never said anything to you concerning such a thing. I quite well understand that as a small official I cannot have the push as you would have, leaving out other qualifications, such as you being more experiences etc. No doubt it is Wallace that have been saying such things thinking that our party will be divided. I can assure you that I together with Brown and the Doctor are doing all we can.

You will read in the S.O.S that the doctor wrote on the blackboard "Vote for Brouwer" now that is not so. When we were all going up to the schoolroom that evening, Brouwer had been to the doctor that afternoon to speak about the piece he published in the S.O.S. Brouwer said that he would say in his speech that "no less a person than Dr. Berkenveld is on the platform backing him." The doctor told him that if he did that he would answer him. Miss Ida wrote on the blackboard vote for Brouwer, and Brouwer after delivered his speech said laughing it looked like the doctor's handwriting. Most of the people had already dispersed and the doctor only said now you are a joker.

Berkenveld has written to Saba. Errol Hassell is the man most against you. He has been to everyone telling them to vote for Brouwer. Halley wrote me that he thinks that Chateau is also trying his best for Brouwer. Up to now I think that you can count on 20 out of 30 voters here. Brown told me that Van Zanten, Leslie, Louis, are entirely against you.

Yes we received the beschikking dividing the officials into categories. I am under the heading Ontv. Kantoren. If I ever get to Curacao I will try and get in the parkette afdeeling. I have now completed strafrecht with Polvliet and have started on strafvordering. Those books from Bais are very dear and badly stenciled. You will also receive enclosed a list of some fellos I think are for you. You can send them a copy of the programme. We had a very bad case of cutting up here last week. One of Samuel Mars sons chopped Paul Courtar twice with a cutlass. Once over the eye even the bone was cut and the other at the back of his head. He is still in hospital and we have Edwy under lock and key. Have you heard who will be appointed in Haayen's place? I hope Mussenden. Some think that Schrils and Mussenden will be made Postdir. Regards from everyone, Very truly your,

Voges"

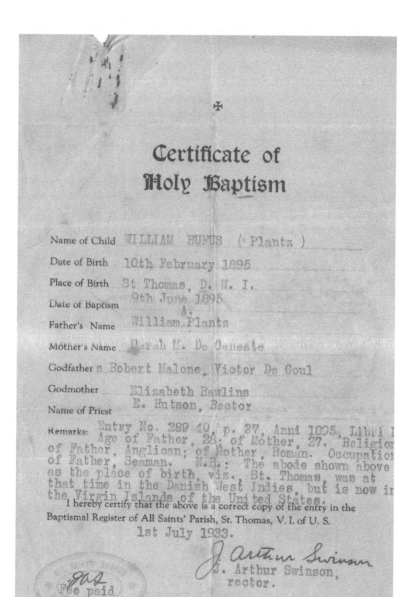

Certificate of
Holy Baptism

Name of Child WILLIAM RUFUS (Plantz)

Date of Birth 10th February 1895

Place of Birth St Thomas, D. W. I.

Date of Baptism 9th June 1895

A.

Father's Name William Plantz

Mother's Name Sarah M. De Ceneste

Godfather s Robert Malone, Victor De Coul

Godmother Elizabeth Rawlins

Name of Priest E. Hutson, Rector

Remarks: Entry No. 289 10, p. 37, Anni 1895, Libri I
Age of Father, 28. of Mother, 27. Religion
of Father, Anglican; of Mother, Roman. Occupation
of Father, Seaman. N.B.: The abode shown above
as the place of birth, viz. St. Thomas, was at
that time in the Danish West Indies, but is now in
the Virgin Islands of the United States.

I hereby certify that the above is a correct copy of the entry in the
Baptismal Register of All Saints' Parish, St. Thomas, V. I. of U. S.

1st July 1933.

J. Arthur Swinson

J. Arthur Swinson,
rector.

Fee paid

SEE REVERSE HEREOF

Document from collection W.R. Plantz estate

In December 1937, William Rufus Plantz was elected as first delegate of the Windward Islands to the senate ('Staten') of the Netherlands Antilles.

The matter of the electoral list still kept people busy, with Broertje Brouwer, the editor of Slag om Slag leading the matter. The Staten would convene for the first time in April 1938 and still the matter regarding the name 'Plantz' had not been resolved as is clear from another letter Mr. Voges sent to him dated January 21, 1938. In this letter he expressed his concern that maybe his name was Geneste after all… If so, his name on the ballot might be considered incorrect, thus possibly prohibiting him from contending in the election. And this was of course the aim of his only opponent: Broertje Brouwer.[xiii]

These first elections were based on census suffrage whereby only people who were literate and owned property could vote.

St.Eustatius, 21 Jan 1938.

Dear Plantz;

As instructed in your letter I am giving the captain
this letter with the enclosed docume nt. I think that
with all these papers you must through. I hope you
are getting help from those chaps down there.
Mally wrote that he also sent you down an"akte van
erkenning floor je moeder". I hope this do not effect
your name Plantz. Sometime ago I believe Daal wrote
us (not officially) that if in the case with children
bo n in St.Kitts who were carrying the fathers name
if they were acknowledged here then they would in
future carry the mother name. This would be the same
with you, you would in future carry de Geneste which
might give them room for agument that the name Plantz
could not have been inserted in the list of voters
and consequently could hot have been entered as
candidate.   Anyway I hope you have some good folks
on your side and will help you fight out.

I guess now that Desertine is in StMaarten he is
helping Brouwer with all sorts of petitions. When
will a decision be made in this matter ? Don't forget
to let me know.
In case you are not accepted send me a radio stating
not granted, you could do without signing it. But if
you are accepted send same in full, now don't forget.
I will see that Brouwer is not elected. Mally wrote
me that if they do not accept you he is sure I can
get the same people to vote for me. Man you know
ifhe gets in he will rip hell for us all.

I have not asked Werkhoven about the cost of this act
but I guess it is free as I made it and he only signed
same. Francis Jane is quite annoyed about Brouwer
putting your certificate in the papers. She told me
today that if he was in Statia he would be horsewipped.
Say try and see if you can bring him up for that
insertion .   I must begin to say I doubt it, but
enquire. You know the law says that the registers are

openbaar, but I don't know how far that izz goes.

On the help of most of the officials yOu can reckon on.
At the beginning I thought that Werkhoven was a B.
man but the other night I heard him giving his opinion
in the presence of the Lampe and Buncamper, and he was
pretty sharp. And he knows that are going to tell it to
Brouwer. Buncamper is still clinging to B. and expects
that you will not be accepted.

Say you might come across men like Clarence Milliard
from here. If you can help them do so for they have
been a great help to me in the election. In fact
help all Statia men, as with the exception of Lejuez
Louis Heyliger the 2 Leslie and Clarence Sprott
every other xxx voter voted for you.

Well I will close hoping that everything is or will
be o.k.

                    Yours truly,

It seems as if not much has changed. In those days there was a lot of melée around election time as well, just like today. It is unclear how much of the melée was picked up by Irving as this was never discussed. He was ten when this all took place so, chances are he did pick up something, but he never talked about it.

By 1938, Irving had been to school on Sint Maarten, Aruba and Curaçao and had passed the eighth-grade exams of the Sint Thomas College, the highest class available on Curaçao. Despite his poor health, his academic results had been excellent.

Since there was no further schooling to be followed on the islands it was decided that he would continue his schooling in the Netherlands.

Irving and his brother Herman Plantz in front of Belvedere,
Collection Ellie Plantz.

His aunt Yvette told me, that on a visit to Europe during her honeymoon in 1937 they avoided visiting Germany and Italy because of the political uncertainty. It is beyond me how, with the threat of hostilities by Germany, he actually departed from the islands in 1938 to enroll in a school in Holland. Is this only due to the benefit of hindsight?

MOVE TO HOLLAND
SECONDARY SCHOOL
1938

So it came to pass that he arrived in the Netherlands by steamship to enroll in the first grade of Rolduc Gymnasium in September.

Irving Plantz with passengers on the Costa Rica, *Collection Ellie Plantz*.

Rolduc, a prominent Roman Catholic boarding school for boys and for aspiring priests in the province of Limburg in the Netherlands was not only selected based on its academic qualities. They had a cricket team - and my father was a fanatical cricket player.

Rolduc is situated near Kerkrade in the South of Limburg, right on the German border. Some of the pastures and orchards that belonged to Rolduc were actually on German soil.

Rolduc in Vogelvlucht - Westzijde

My father never talked much about this experience. But just imagine you are 14 years old and arrive by boat in a country far away from home. Everything is different. And you do not know anybody. I understand that his trip had been prepared with the help of one of the Fraters of his school in Curaçao. I remember a picture in an old photo album of a young man wearing a coat which was far too wide and too long for him, hat in his hand - the wardrobe of an adult, ill-chosen and inappropriate for a tall, slightly-built 14-year-old boy.

My sister Yvette recalls him telling her that his father came to visit him at boarding school. That he smoked cigars and drank wine with him and felt so bad afterwards, with the corridors at school caving in on him, that he thought it must have been the effect of the cigars. It probably was the first time he ever was drunk. This visit probably took place before Holland was invaded by the Germans, so before May 10, 1940. It seems unlikely that this took place during the war.

Name tag from Rolduc. *Collection Ellie Plantz*

To get an idea of his daily routine at school the Rolduc yearbooks provide a fountain of information. The Rolduc yearbooks for the period 1938 – 1944, which I have researched, contain a day-by-day record of the most important things that happened during his formative years at boarding school. They present a setting which gives an idea of the overwhelming impressions that this young, brown skinned, Caribbean 14-year-old, far away from home, must have experienced: the extreme cold, the rigour of boarding school life in a Roman Catholic seminary, the different culture, education in Dutch as primary language, food, and clothing.

These impressions alone are enough to daunt any pupil starting on his own, in a new country, a new environment. There were enough reasons for his academic studies to falter as a result. But they did not. Academically he did very well, as is evidenced by the yearbooks. The school gave out annual prizes and honorary mentions for academic results and he was awarded many of these. From the 3rd through the 5th grade, among other prizes and honorary mentions, he won first prize for English. And this for English which will have been quite different to the English he was used to in Sint Maarten.

Irving Plantz with classmates at Rolduc 1939. Collection Ellie Plantz

Rolduc

THE IMPACT OF ROLDUC SCHOOL

It is clear that the years at Rolduc from 1938 to 1944 and the rest of the Second World War had an important and lasting influence on his life. Three factors stand out.

First of all, life at a Catholic boarding school and seminary with a strong focus on religious celebration meant that there was a strong religious discipline within the school. Mass every day, sometimes twice a day. The yearbooks paint a picture of a devout alumni group. Celebration of the name days of the saints, funerals of fellow pupils and old priests who attended Rolduc were major events. He learned the Latin rites, the Gregorian chants and even briefly considered becoming a priest. I had a father who never missed a weekly mass and obliged us to go as it was our duty to God. In the recent past Rolduc has been mentioned in the context of the abuse scandals that have tainted the Catholic Church. This has left us wondering whether my father ever witnessed or maybe even experienced any of that. For the love of our father, we push this thought far from our minds.

Secondly, his exposure to the natural phenomenon of seasons and weather changes, most in particular the extreme cold he had to endure.

The winter seasons he experienced at Rolduc were described in the yearbooks as particularly harsh. This had its impact on the health of the teachers and the pupils. The yearbooks describe how the infirmary at the boarding school would be filled to overflowing with boys so sick that they had to be moved to nearby hospitals.

On more than one occasion a young student died. A dreadful loss of young life and an impressionable experience for his peers.

It has been said that my father fought the cold in his boarding school years by wearing newspapers between multiple layers of clothes. And as he quickly grew to become a tall lanky youth, I have often wondered how he continued to acquire clothes that fit, even during the war. He never liked the cold and avoided it if he could. The impact on his health and in particular the weakness of his lungs may have contributed to his eventual demise on May 1, 1987.

Irving Plantz with classmates at Rolduc 1943.
Collection Ellie Plantz

Thirdly, and this goes without saying, living through the Second World War, far away from his family, left its indelible mark on the man he became. During the war it was impossible to maintain contact with his parents on the other side of the ocean. Until the United States joined the war there was some contact through his aunt Helen Cave who lived on Staten Island, New York. She was able to send letters and care packages by way of the Red Cross. This stopped after the United States joined the war after the attack on Pearl Harbour.

The yearbooks are not clear about when my father actually left the school. One scenario, which is the most probable, is that he stayed at Rolduc until his graduation in June 1944[xiv]. The date on his final diploma is the same date as referred to in the Rolduc yearbook 1943-1944 as the date that the diplomas were handed out.[xv]

But another scenario could be that he may have left in December 1943. The yearbook mentions in an entry dated December 8th [xvi], that the general expectation was that the Germans would be interning all the older boys in their final school year as forced laborers for the 'Arbeitseinsatz' to work in camps in Germany. The yearbook 1942-1943 already mentions in an entry dated May 27, 1943 where the 1943 graduation of the final class is described:

"Congratulations to all. How awful that the next thought must be, how best can I go into hiding as soon as possible…?"[xvii]

My father was at least 2 years older than his classmates, having only started his curriculum in Holland at 14 whilst the standard age was 12. The yearbook mentions that a special law was adopted to ensure that for those who had done well at their December tests, these tests could count as emergency final exam, should they be interned before the final exams would be taken.

The yearbook talks about at least three classmates who made use of this option. Instead of signing up for the work camps they chose to go into hiding. It is further odd that the yearbook mentions in two entries dated on June 14th, 1944, respectively June 16th, 1944, that all 14 pupils had successfully passed the Gymnasium A exam.[xviii] However, the list of pupils having successfully passed this exam mentions 16 names. The Rolduc records are sealed for 100 years and it is difficult to get access without special dispensation.

Verifying the time when exactly my father left secondary school to go into hiding has so far not been possible.

So, either in December 1943 or in June 1944, school was out. And my father too went into hiding to avoid being interned and sent to a work camp in Germany.

My father hardly ever spoke about this period of his life. There was a silent consensus at home, that the war was too horrible a subject to talk about, not something he wanted to be reminded of. So, we did not ask and he did not tell.

WAR YEARS

I had only one conversation with my father about this period. While he was on a business trip in Holland in 1977, he came to my student apartment for dinner on May 4th. This is the day that Holland commemorates those who have fallen in the war with solemn ceremonies celebrated at different locations. Two of these ceremonies are usually televised. This was also the case that evening. We watched the ceremony in the Nieuwe Kerk in Amsterdam, followed by a public ceremony on Dam square which was attended by Queen Juliana. I watched my father looking at the television with tears in his eyes as the crowd respected the one-minute silence.

Immediately afterwards, the television showed a short impression of the ceremony on the Waalsdorper vlakte in de dunes of the Hague and Wassenaar. Many people who had been active in the resistance movement were executed there by firing squad, including one young Antillean boy he knew well. Boy Ecury from Aruba. Boy was only two years his senior. My father was visibly emotional. For a while he just sat there, silently...

And then he started to talk. For the first and last time he consciously started to relate some of his war time experience. I say consciously as later I saw him relive a scary episode when, battling with cancer and heavily sedated with painkillers, he hallucinated vividly. I have often wondered what exactly happened but will never know and out of respect for him have refrained from finding out more than he was prepared to tell.

It is a long time ago and I will record my recollection as best as possible, realizing that along the way some of the facts may have been embellished, as we inevitably do with cherished memories. No story he ever told me was so personal. It deserves to be recorded from his perpective. So, I decide to let him 'speak':

"The war time was very hard. People don't realize that today. I still think that many hoped that Holland would not be caught up in a war and would be able to claim neutrality as it had done in the First World War.

They were well prepared at Rolduc, very mindful of the responsibility they had for so many young pupils. When the war started there was a lot of anxiety among the teachers. They tried to hide that.

First came the German airplanes that flew over Rolduc on May 10th. School went on and everything was 'business as usual'. But our attention was more on what was happening outside in the sky.

The next day we saw the first German soldiers. Two high ranking officers came to order the director to take down the Dutch flags that were flying over the school. This was also the first day we had a drill to test how to get to the air-raid shelter that had been prepared.

The day after we saw the German invasion from close by. In the evening a long column of German military vehicles arrived on the grounds of Rolduc to stay over night. There must have been over 400 soldiers. They left the next day. Luckily Rolduc did not have more German guests after that. And then the Dutch army gave up. Within four days, the Germans took control.

Life at Rolduc continued but the effects of the war became noticeable. Smaller food rations, hardly any meat. Dutch students received care packages from home. Luckily, I continued to get mail and sometimes a care package from Aunt Helen in New York through the Red Cross. But this stopped after the United States joined the war in December 1941. Just before that I had received the last news from home and would receive no more until after the war.

In the winters it was colder inside. There was little coal to keep the heating going. I slept in my clothes and used newspaper as extra lining. At one point during my last school year the priests at Rolduc told to me that they had little confidence in the Gover-

nor of the Dutch region Seyss-Inquart. Young men were being interned to work in Germany for the war effort. They were worried as I fell into the age category that was targeted and were uncertain if they could arrange for me to be exempted whilst in school. They told me that I would have to go into hiding and that they would arrange this. I was lucky that I could go into hiding with the family of a fellow student in Limburg. The arrangement was that I would have to help out on their farm in return. This went well until someone from the resistance advised the family that a traitor had betrayed them and that the Germans would come to raid their home.

Irving Plantz the Limburg family in 1944. *Collection Ellie Plantz*

The resistance took over and brought me and two other men to a farmer in Drenthe, where we could stay, again… as long as we helped out on the farm.

Irving Plantz with farmers in Drenthe in 1944. *Collection Ellie Plantz*

One day while working on the farm, we saw a group of German cars moving towards the farm and we fled, thinking that again our benefactors had been betrayed.

I did not know where to go. I knew some Antillean students in Tilburg and decided to go there. But I was not sure where they would be. Like me they had probably gone into hiding. I had to hide from the Germans. So, I travelled by night and hid by day. When I reached Tilburg, I found Jules de Windt and Tirzo Sprockel. I was able to stay there for a while and a lot happened....

So much, that there came a time when it was best for me to leave again. I decided to try to go to Beverwijk where Hyacinth Connor was living before the war with the Van den Berg family, the parents of his girlfriend. I hoped he would still be there and would be able to help. If not, I knew nobody else and had no other place else to go. So, travelling by night, jumping on trains and hiding during the day, it took me about eight days to reach Beverwijk. I was exhausted and hungry.

When I finally reached the Van den Berg home, I knocked on the door. It was opened and I asked: "Does Hyacinth Connor live here?". The brusque answer was... No... and the door was closed. I was desperate. No place to go. So, I sat down on the sidewalk and thought: "...if the Germans pick me up now, at least they will have to feed me..."

Engagement picture Hyacinth Connor and Jo van de Berg.
Collection Ellie Plantz

Behind me the door opened again and Mrs Van de Berg told me that she had some soup and some bread for me in the kitchen, but that I would have to leave once I had eaten that. You can imagine how good that soup tasted after not having had anything to eat for a couple of days. And whilst I was eating the soup, Hyacinth appeared and sat down with me.

He was in hiding nearby in a haystack owned by the Seignette family, your mother's family...

Mrs Van den Berg apologized. They just wanted to be sure that I could be trusted and was not there to betray Hyacinth. I could stay and went into hiding in the same haystack where Hyacinth had been holed up, together with a Jewish professor.

As there were not many people around who spoke any decent English, our knowledge of English came in handy. We were able to help the resistance to communicate with downed parachutists. And when the Canadians finally came, we were asked to go with them on the jeeps from village to village to act as interpreters.

Anyway, I ended up travelling back home on the first ship that was going to Curaçao after the war. I had no way of letting my parents know that I was coming. On the ship were many wives of Shell employees who happened to be in Holland when the war broke out.

My father was an important man at the time and was delegated by the government to meet the ship coming in. When he saw me coming down the gangway, he simply left all the formalities and took me home to Van Engelenweg. My mother did not believe I was back. She went into a kind of shock. I sat next to her on the front porch for the longest while. She would just stare ahead and from time to time look at me from the corners of her eyes, hardly turning her head. When I tried to hug her, she shrugged off my arm. I think she had resigned herself to the fact that I might be dead and now had to deal with the unbelievable reality that by some stroke of luck I had survived the war and was in fact alive.

Anyway, I stayed on Curaçao for a while and also went to Sint Maarten. It must have been for some 8 weeks. I went back to Holland after that to enroll in the University of Amsterdam to study law. Going back on the ship I took along a lot of stuff for the families that had helped me. The Van den Berg family and their neighbors, the Seignette family, your mother's family.

Your grandmother, Valentine, had done herself proud. To express her thanks to these Dutch families she packed everything from coffee, tea, sugar, flour, cigarettes and chocolate bars to ladies' fine stockings and material to make dresses. And because your aunt Han was getting married soon, she had bought a big role of nice fabric for her wedding dress. When I came back to Holland, I lived with the family Van den Berg for a while, together with Hyacinth before I moved to Amsterdam."

…That was it. His war story. The one he never talked about. I knew I had to stay put during this monologue. Hearing him talk about his war experience was mindboggling. I had so many questions but did not dare to ask them. It was clear that that was it, no more war talk…

The spell was over. There are pictures of him in this period, including pictures with the families where he was hiding. I even found a series of pictures of him visiting the Waalsdorpervlakte after the war...

Irving Plantz at Waalsdorpervlakte after the war.
Collection Ellie Plantz

AFTER THE WAR (1945 – 1952)

Studying law – Courting my mother

After the war Irving went back to the Antilles - first to Curacao and then to Sint Maarten - before returning to the Netherlands to enroll in the Law Faculty of the University of Amsterdam.

My mother could tell me very little about knowing him during the war time. She told me that she knew of the two dark boys living with the Van den Berg family after the war, that they had been hiding in a haystack during the war. She told me about how after the war she got to know my father.

She was working in a food distribution office after the war. She told me that at one point she needed a date for an office party, because the boy she secretly had a crush on had asked her best friend. She did not want to show up without a date. So, her mother suggested that she should go and ask one of the nice dark boys at the Van den Berg family. She set out to ask Hyacinth, who she knew better from the tennisclub.

But since he was not at home and, after all, he was engaged to be married to Jo van den Berg, she ended up asking my father to go with her. And he said yes. He must have been nervous to go to the house to pick her up. My mother was one of nine children, one of seven daughters. What could he bring as a guest for all the family? But he thought of something: he stuffed his coat pocket with chocolate which he had brought back from Curaçao to pass around. My mother' sisters made sure that she would go out with him again, hoping for more chocolate. The inevitable happened; they fell in love…

Irving Plantz and Ellie Seignette (later Plantz) at Wijk aan Zee beach.
Collection Ellie Plantz

Following the curriculum at the law faculty, Irving studied hard and eventually moved to Amsterdam. He continued to court my mother who had also moved to Amsterdam. Together they moved in circles of Dutch Antillean students around town. His father, William Rufus, was a regular visitor to Holland in view of his involvement with politics, so he saw him often. And when he got engaged to my mother, my grandfather bought her diamond engagement ring.

Antillean students. *Collection Ellie Plantz*

Writing 'Ole Tales' – Returning to the Caribbean

It is in this period, whilst studying in Amsterdam that he, like some other Dutch Caribbean students, was approached to participate in the new programming of Radio Nederland Wereldomroep aimed at the Dutch Caribbean. This prompted him to write the stories. It is unclear when exactly he started or how many stories were broadcast, but from the material found by Dr. Jos de Roo we know that in any case there were at least 18 stories broadcast over the period February 1949 to December 1952.

In 1952 Charles Irving Plantz graduated as Master at Law from the University of Amsterdam.

On November 1, 1952 he married my mother. On November 7 he read his two last contributions to the Radio Nederland Wereldomroep programming, one broadcast on November 8 and the last one broadcast on December 31, 1952. On November 20th, 1952 the newlyweds left by KLM 635, the PH-TPI 'Prinses Irene' to Curacao, via Glasgow, Gander, Montreal and Havana. There were 14 passengers on board.

Upon arrival they temporarily took up residence at my grandparents' residence at Van Engelenweg 29.

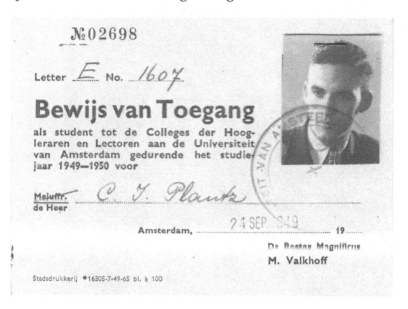

№02698

Letter *E* No. *1607*

Bewijs van Toegang

als student tot de Colleges der Hoogleraren en Lectoren aan de Universiteit van Amsterdam gedurende het studiejaar 1949—1950 voor

Mejuffr.
de Heer *C. J. Plantz*

Amsterdam, 24 SEP. 1949 19

De Rector Magnificus
M. Valkhoff

Stadsdrukkerij #16305-7-49-65 bl. à 100

Wedding picture Irving and Ellie Plantz, Amsterdam November 1, 1952.
Collection Ellie Plantz

Funny English

Before we go into the stories…...

First time visitors to the Caribbean who have a fair command of English love to hear the sing song tones but may not always fully understand what is being said. The 'Ole Tales, sweet memories' have been recorded phonetically to mimick the sound of the Sint Maarten English in order to facilitate the reading for the broadcast.

My mother first encountered this 'funny English' after she travelled to the Curaçao in 1952, after marrying my father. As housing was scarce, they first lived with my grandparents on the Van Engelenweg. It was not easy as a young couple to have an uninsulated bedroom next to that of your parents (in law)-especially in this case, because the springs of the bed creaked with every little movement. Apprehensive that every time they turned the parents (in law) might think that they 'were at it again...' my mother resorted to greasing the springs using a toothbrush and Brylcream, not that that helped a lot.

My mother made friends on the island. And as my father play-ed cricket for the Asiento team, she met the wives of some of the players from England who were employed by Shell and lived in Emmastad or Julianadorp. She once told me that whilst living with my grandparents she had invited one of her English friends for tea. My grandmother, who always was a proud hostess made sure that there were cookies and cakes in abundance. And although she did not participate in the conversation, she made the following comment when this proper English lady left: "*Wha Elly, she a nice lady but she talk funny English eh…"* I am very curious to know what my mother's English friend thought of my grandmother's Sint Maarten English.

This live experience of the variety of languages that are called English is also reflected in a scene of the script of 'My fair lady', a musical written by Alan Jay Lerner which premiered in 1956, where Henry Higgins expresses his despair to Colonel Pickering about the development of the English language even within England:

"PICKERING: *I beg your pardon.*
HIGGINS
An Englishman's way of speaking absolutely classifies him.
The moment he talks, he makes some other Englishmen despise him.
One common language I'm afraid we'll never get.
Oh why can't the English learn to- Set a good example to people, whose
English, is painful to your ears.
The Scotch and the Irish leave you close to tears!
There are even places where English completely disappears,
Why, in America they haven't used it for years. Why can't the English teach
their children how to speak?
Norwegians learn Norwegian; the Greeks are taught their Greek.
In France every Frenchman knows his language from 'A' to 'Zed'- But the
French don't care what they do, actually, so long as they pronounce it properly.
Arabians learn Arabian with the speed of summer lightning.
The Hebrews learn it backwards which is absolutely frightening.
Use proper English, you're regarded as a freak. Oh why can't the English- Why
can't the English learn to speak?"

Caribbean English

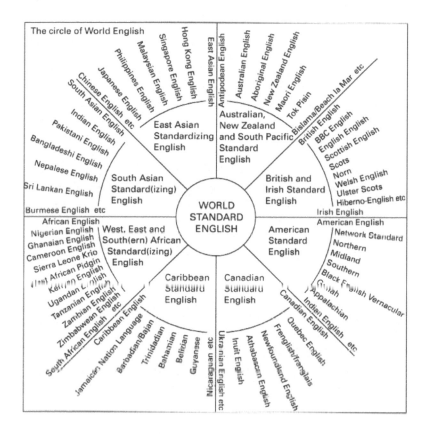

The circle of World English

WORLD STANDARD ENGLISH

East Asian Standardizing English

Australian, New Zealand and South Pacific Standard English

British and Irish Standard English

South Asian Standard(izing) English

West, East and South(ern) African Standard(izing) English

American Standard English

Caribbean Standard English

Canadian Standard English

Hong Kong English · East Asian English · Antipodean English · Australian English · Aboriginal English · New Zealand English · Maori English · Tok Pisin · Bislama/Beach la Mar etc · British English · BBC English · English English · Scottish English · Scots · Norn · Welsh English · Ulster Scots · Hiberno-English etc · Irish English · American English · Network Standard · Northern · Midland · Southern · Black English Vernacular · Gullah · Appalachian · Indian English etc · Inuit English · Athabascan English · Newfoundland English · Frenglish/franglais · Quebec English · Canadian English · Ukranian English etc · Nicaraguan · Guyanese · Belizian · Bahamian · Trinidadian · Barbadian/Bajan · Jamaican Nation Language · Caribbean English · South African English etc · Zimbabwean English · Zambian English · Tanzanian English · Ugandan English · Kenyan English · (West) African Pidgin · Sierra Leone Krio · Cameroon English · Ghanaian English · Nigerian English · African English · Burmese English etc · Sri Lankan English · Nepalese English · Bangladeshi English · Pakistani English · Indian English · South Asian English · Chinese English etc · Japanese English · Philippines English · Malaysian English · Singapore English

Sint Maarten English can be grouped in the Caribbean English section. As far as I know there is no official orthography, grammar or syntax for Sint Maarten English.[xix] And whilst within the Caribbean English section in McArthurs[xx] Circle other English languages are named which may or may not lay claim to having an official grammar and syntax, I would dare to say that within the Caribbean we tend to understand each other whether we come from Trinidad, Barbados, Jamaica, Guyana or indeed the officially Dutch Sint

Maarten and French Saint Martin, whenever we use our variety of Sint Maarten English.

The English spoken in the Caribbean is often referred to as 'pidgin English'[xxi]. This term is incorrect in so far as a pidgin language is considered a simplified means of communication that develops naturally when speakers of two or more languages need to understand each other. Pidgin has no native speakers. When the pidgin used develops into a natural language and nativised into a primary language it is commonly referred to as 'creole'.[xxii] Our Sint Maarten English is therefore more a creole language then it is a pidgin language, because we 'speak' it as our mother tongue.

Whilst in this day and age, with our students studying abroad, wider education of our people, popularization of travel, international entertainment and internet have all resulted in most of our people being able to speak a more standard form of English to engage with others on their travels or with visitors to our island, we tend to revert to our Sint Maarten English when seeking comfort or expressing ourselves in excitement, easily slipping in and out.

Mervyn Morris, (born 1937) the Jamaican poet laureate has expressed this accurately in his essay *'Is English we speaking'* [xxiii] where he wrote:

"For most West Indians the language of feeling, their most intimate language, is creole. It has been observed that West Indians who seem entirely comfortable in standard English often break into creole in moments of excitement or agitation."

Two questions come to mind when considering the fact that Sint Maarten English is the lingua franca of Sint Maarten/Saint Martin:

1. How come the English prevalently spoken in the Caribbean is so different from the original 'Queens English'?

2. Why is English prevalently spoken by the local population of Sint Maarten/Saint Martin instead of Dutch and French?

To start to understand, we need to delve into the history of the Caribbean region and that of Sint Maarten/Saint Martin. Without expanding into much detail, the following facts are relevant for the development of Caribbean English and give an explanation for why Sint Maarten English is spoken on Sint Maarten/Saint Martin.

Since the discovery by Columbus on his voyages since 1492, the Caribbean region saw a convergence of many different cultures. Colonial expeditions from Spain, Portugal, England, Holland, France and even Denmark and Sweden, driven by imperial rivalries and economic ambition, set out to conquer and settle the discovered islands, hoping to establish a profitable source of income or necessary source of certain commodities or food staples for the mother land.

In the early 1500s the first Africans were introduced as slaves in the Americas by the Spanish and Portuguese. From the early 1700s, hundredthousands of people were transported to the Caribbean, particularly from West Africa, to work as slaves on the plantations.

Initially workers on the colonial plantations in the Caribbean would have spoken a variety of ethnic languages. But the language that was imposed on them in the English colonies by the slave owners was English. Among the workers themselves, a pidgin language would have been used, based on the sounds, vocabulary and simplified grammatical structures of all the contributing languages. This in turn was combined with the English to come to a common means of communication. Overtime this pidgin variety became the norm and was what the children learned. The pidgin was thereby nativised to a primary language, a mother tongue. That is how the Caribbean English language family started.

Sint Maarten English

Sint Maarten was discovered by Columbus on his second discovery voyage on November 11, 1493 and was named after the saint of that day, Saint Martin of Tours and claimed as Spanish territory. The Dutch, French and English were very interested in the Island and contested each other for dominion.

Then, after having been abandoned by the Spanish in 1648, the island was occupied almost simultaneaously by the Dutch and the French. Some initial skirmishes occurred between them to claim dominion of the island. In the end the division of the island was settled amicably in the Treaty of Concordia, signed on March 23, 1648. The negotiated coexistence continues to this day, even though the borders have not always been open.

Over time tobacco and sugar plantations were operated and various salt ponds exploited both on the Dutch and the French side. Although the Dutch flag flew over the Dutch side and the Treaty of Concordia was signed on behalf of the Prince of Orange, who was the Dutch regent at the time, the island was governed for the Dutch by English mercenaries conscripted into the Dutch navy. Due to the lack of interest of Dutch settlers to establish posts on the island, British settlers were invited to set up home and were given land in property as long as they brought along the labor force, consisting of slaves. The use of pidgin English variety followed, as it had in the wider Caribbean region wherever English settlers prevailed.

In 1943, during the Second World War, the United States built Princess Juliana Airport in order to have an airbase from which to fight against German submarines. This helped to Americanize the population of Sint Maarten/Saint Martin, and English became the working language for both the French and the Dutch side.

Whilst Dutch and French remained the official language of the governmental administration on either side, Sint Maarten English became and remains the prevailing spoken language on Sint Maarten/Saint Martin.

The English of 'Ole tales, sweet memories'

'Ole tales, sweet memories' consists of stories written down between 1949 and 1952, with the sole purpose of reading them for a radio broadcast aimed at a windward island audience. When my father typed out the stories, I believe he never thought they would serve any other purpose then as guidance notes to him when reading the stories in the broadcast. His grades in school for English were actually excellent and the English taught at Rolduc in Limburg surely had nothing to do with Sint Maarten English.

So, writing the stories with that purpose in mind and intending to give the audience a good dose of the sweet Sint Maarten sound, he was not hindered by an official orthography or syntax of Sint Maarten English. His practical solution was to use an almost phonetic spelling, reflecting as much as possible the sound that was familiar to him as the language he spoke and heard back home. Making typos or being consistent in the way he wrote things down probably did not matter, as he was the only one, he thought, who would ever read the texts. I have tried to take out some of the very clear typos and to bring some consistency but have done this sparsely in order to protect the integrity of the texts as much as possible, whilst accommodating the future readers he never expected to be. To that end I have given each story the 'working title' as given to the stories by Dr. Jos de Roo in his thesis 'Praatjes voor de West -De Wereldomroep en de Antilliaanse en Surinaamse Literatuur 1947-1958' title, and have chosen the title for the book as 'Ole tales, sweet memories'

So, this is how I recommend that you read the stories. I have prepared a Glossary which may help you, where words used are indicated in alphabetical order next to their more common 'Standard English' meaning. Sometimes I include more information that may be useful for your understanding or interesting to give the island color. More often than not the meaning will have to be derived from the context in which the word is used.

Do not expect the use of Standard English when reading the stories in 'Ole tales, sweet memories'. In Sint Maarten English there is no formal syntax, simple or no conjugation of verbs. There is no clear distinction between present, past, perfect and future tense, for example "*she tell me last week*" instead of "*she told me last week*". The indefinite article 'a' and 'an' are scarce and where used seldom reflects the 'n' if the next word starts with a vowel. Mixed use of singular for plural, singular often used when the plural meaning is intended. Let the context guide you to derive the meaning.

There is sometimes a conspicuous absence of the verb 'to be', for example as in "*he is walking*", it will not be unusual to find it reflected as "*he walkin*". As reflected in this example when using the '–ing' form of a verb to reflect the present, past or perfect continuous tense, in Sint Maarten English we simply drop the 'g' at the end and emphasize the 'n' in our pronunciation. In the Glossary I have only taken up such examples of the '–ing' form of verbs, if it is entirely clear whether this is an instance where in Standard English the '–ing' form of a verb is used or not, or the meaning of the verb itself may need further clarification.

Note that the pronouns may not be used as you would expect, for example: a subject pronoun may be used as object as in "*I like she*" instead of "*I like her*", or a subject pronoun may be used as genitive as in "*that he donkey*" instead of "that is his donkey". I have tried to reflect this in the Glossary, but again it is the context that will have to guide you.

The pronunciation in Sint Maarten English also differs from standard English. Some examples that are very noticeable when you hear Sint Maarten English being spoken are the following

1. <th> in words such as think and three is pronounced using a <t> sound and in words such as this and that using a <d> sound.
2. initial <h> is deleted in words such as happy and house, saying "*appy*" and "*ome*".
3. simplification of complex strings of consonants by deleting the final sound, so that best becomes "*bes*", respect becomes "*respeck*" and land becomes "*lan*".
4. the <r> sound is surpressed after a vowel in words like hard as "*had*", corn as "con" and nurse as "nus".
5. Words like ground, town, around pronounced as "*grung*", "*tung*", "*arung*".
6. Words ending on –ing will be pronounced dropping the 'g' and emphasizing the 'n'.
7. The 'I' sound rounded and pronounced as 'oi', as in "*I reminded him*" as "*Oi remoind him*"
8. As far as I know there is only one sound clip left of all the recordings made of the 'Ole Tales'.

Ole tales, Sweet Memories…
these are some of the stories
he told….

Damfool and sensible

Broadcast February 19,1949

A gon tell you a story mah Granmother tole me when a was a lil boy. In years gone by there lived a ole lady who had two children and because one was doting and the other one wasn't everybody called the dotin one Damfool and the other Sensible. Nobody knew they real names and nobody cared to know them.

Sensible use to work on a plantation all day to keep up his mother and brother, and Damfool used to weed the lil garden while his mother watched, fraid he would pull out the potatoes and carrots instead of the weeds.

If the mother was cooking on her coalpots outside he'ed be standing around and if she was cleaning the house he follow her from room to room till she get vex and tell him to go outside to lay on he back and look at the sky. Hours later he would call out to her *"Mammy, wa a mus look at now, a tired a lookin at the sky"*.

But one day Mammy get sick from ole age and when they call the doctor he tell them that they must take good care of her and give her a spoon full of the medicine he give them and that every night she must have a hot bad as hot as she could stand.

During the first days Sensible stay home from his work to tend to his mother, but when she staid sick he had to go to the plantation and let his brother take care of Mammy. So every day Damfool woud give his mother her medicine and feed her with the porridge his brother had cook. And when Sensible would come home from his work, Damfool would have hot water ready for him to bade his mother, they use to bade her behind the house in a big copper in which Damfool had to throw the boilin water and add as much cold that his mother could stand.

But one day Sensible cut heself with his machete when he was cutting cane and they bring him home and put him to bed. So that day Damfool had to take care of his brother and mother. When the time come to bade his mother, he put her outside in the copper and throw seven buckets of well water in it like he use to, but he forgot to throw in boiling water. When Sensible hear her scream he called out to his brother "*The water ain hot enough*". So Damfool, instead a throwing in hot water, he put a fire under the copper, piling up the firewood faster than it could burn and he keep on thinking:

" *The doctor say it must be hot. The hotter the better and the sooner Mammy get well.*"

So the water got hotter and hotter and when Mammy started to grin from the pain he called out to his brother

"*Mammy feeling better, already she is laughing at me and the water aint even hot.*"

And when Mammy let out a scream and try to jump out he cried to Sensible:

"*Man, she jumpin an laughin already.*"

In the end Mammy was cooked to death with Damfool calling out to his brother that now they mother was better and that she was sleeping with her mouth open.

That is the story how Damfool killed his mother but what happened to him and Sensible a don know.

The sensiblest man of the world

Broadcast April 16, 1949

Wen a was a lil boy a use to like to hear stories, an a suppose all lil children like to hear them. Every country got its own fairy tales and a suppose lots of these are made by the fathers but especially by the mothers just to keep they children quiet.

The last time a told you the story about how Damfool cook he mother, an today a got another old story to tell you. Tis funny but most of the stories you hear when you are young are about talking animals or trees or about foolish and sensible people, and most of the stories are cruel and the children seem to like them this way.

This time a gon tell you the story about the man who wanted to know everything, and so to be the sensiblest man in the world.

In days gone by in some country or other they lived a man who used to say to heself: *"A must try to learn all a can an to work as hard as a can an then a'll be the smartest man in the world and everybody will come to see me and aks me advice and then a gon be rich because to get a answer they gon to pay me a lotta money."*

So this man use to work and he use to aks everybody a lot of questions about everything he saw. He use to try an talk to foreigners to learn dey language and if somebody tole him something was so an so he would always try an fine out if tha was true. When he hear tha the stars in the sky an the hairs on ye head was uncountable, he try to count them.

When he hear the story about how the animals use to talk to one another on old years night, he tried to hear them talk an to learn their language too. But though he talked and listened to dogs and cats, cows and horses, they nevered answered him but he never gave up hope an he said to heslef: *"A suppose dey wont talk when a listen, and maybe dey can even understand me, because a don't talk they language, so first a must learn dey language an then we can talk. They must know a lot a kin use an if a kin speak to animals people from all over the world will come to see me an a can even act as a doctor for animals, because a'll know when they feel sick."*

One day when he was talking to an old man he was told about the root people use to use long ago when dey wanted to talk or listen to animals. He aks the old man if he know what the root look like. But the old fellow had only heard about it but had never seen it he said. *"If you go up in the mountains an look good and hard ye might find it."*

So the next day the inquisitive man went up in the mountains to look. He climbed and climbed, looked and looked until he got tired. Then he lay down an rested an afterwards started to such and look again. On the third day he went in a cave to sleep but it wasn't a cave, only a hole in the mountains through which he came in a small valley with great trees and of all the trees he saw, there was only one he recognized, a great big bloddaytree. He went an sat under this tree to rest. He was nearly asleep, when he hear somebody say: *"Ayo looka trouble. Man wha you doin here?"*.

He look around, but there was nobody. Then he hear: *"Tis me the blodday. Wha you doin here?"*

So he turned around an tole the tree the story about how he was trying to find the wonderroot and how so come he find the entrance to the valley. When he finish the tree started to laugh an say:

"Man you lucky you find me, you don have to look any more for the root. A know where to find it. But if a tell you, you wont know where to look in all these mountains." And the man say: *"Come quick an show me."* But the tree anser: *"A aint allowed to leave me place but a kin help you. A kin turn you in a blodday so you can take me place, then a kin go get the root for you."*

"Hurry then", the man said, *"...an come back quick"*.

So the blodday turn the man in a tree an heself in a man and he went off and left the valley, and a suppose the man must still be waitin for the tree to return with the wonderroot.

Til another time.

The three lil pigs

Breakfast June 4, 1949

A pig father had three lil pig sons and he worked hard to make good pigs outta them. He teach them to work for themselves and to keep outta trouble. When they had come old enough, he calls them, give them all the advice he could an told them all he knew about the worl. He gave each of his sons a dollar an warn them to look out for the ole wise wolf and to go an try to make a living for themself, because he had come too ole to work for he big sons.

"Remember", he said: *"be kind an polite to everybody an show that a give you a good education, otherwise a can be proud a you. An don ever forget ye ole father!"*

So the three lil pigs lef the house, they father wave them goodbye an he thought: *"a wonder wha gon become a them, a shouden-a leave them go yet."*

The lil pigs walked along the road and looked at the new things they had never seen before. They hadden been so far from home in they life and now they father waooen with them to tell all they wanted to know. They walked and walked and when they get tired they rested an eat some a the turnips they father had give them, to take along.

When they met a man with a big bunch of straw on he back, the first lil pig said: *"Good morning Mister, can ye please tell me how much the straw ye got there cost?"* *"Sure Piggy"*, the man said: *"if ye got a dollar ye can have the whole bunch."* The lil pig give the man he dollar, said solong to he brothers an lef the road with he bundle a straw. When he find a place he liked, he started to build a one-room house. After he had worked hard all day the house was finish and he lay down an because he very tired he fell asleep right-away an he sleep till the next morning late. When he look outta the window the nex morning he see the ole wolf comin down the road an because he remembered the advice he father give him he stay in the house. But the wolf walked right up to the door an knocked.

"Wha ye want", the lil pig ask. "A want to look at ye house", the wolf said. "Go away, a ain go let ye in. "Then a gon blow ye house dung an eat you." "Go away", the lil pig answered getting frighten. So the wolf huffed and puffed an blow the house dung an eat the first lil pig.

The other two pigs walked along until they meet a man with a great big bunch a sticks. The second lil pig pay the man a dollar an he got enough sticks to build a house. He wave goodbye to he brother and build he house near the river on a lil hill so he could look out on all sides. One morning the ole wolf who was hungry an feelin like eating pork-chops knocked on his door and aks to be let in. But jus like he brother had done the lil pig refuse. An the wolf warn him he would blow his house dung an eat him, but still the lil pig wouden open up.

So the wolf huffed and puffed, an huffed and puffed an at first he couden blow the house down. But he got hungrier all the time so tried harder and huffed and puffed an huffed an puffed an in the end he blow the house dung an eat the second lil pig.

The third lil pig walked till he come up with a man with a wheelbarrow fulla bricks. An the man like the lil pig because he was so polite so he sell him the bricks and lend the wheelbarrow to carry them in.

So the lil pig build a brick house and because he had too much bricks he made double walls. After he had work hard for a week the house was ready and he started to gather food for the winter. One day when he was coming home he see the wolf in the distance running to cut him off but the lil pig throw dung he bundle a potatoes and run like he had never run before, an he just had time to shut the door an lock before the wolf reach it.

Right away the wolf started to huff and puff and huff and puff but he couden blow the house down because it was very strong.

An because he was hungry he had to go look for food somewhere else.

Nex day the wolf caught the lil pig while he was up in a apple tree and he lay down under the tree so the pig was afraid to come down. The lil pig waited and waited and thought and thought how he could get the wolf to go away. Then he thought of something. *"Do you want a nice apple?"* he aks the wolf. *"Sure, throw me the biggest one ye can find, a like apple sauce an pork chops"*, the wolf answered. With all his might [he threw an apple] right in the face a the wolf, an because the apple was so hard it blind the wolf in both eyes. He ran off howling and because he couden see where he was going, he run straight in the river and got drowned.

That is how the third lil pig got rid a the ole wise wolf who had eaten his brothers.

Ole Johannes and the cotton thieves

Broadcast February 11, 1950

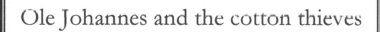

Ah been wondering if ayo kno the story about Ole Johannes an the cotton thieves, how they use to steal a lotta cotton from Jo and tho he use to try all kinds a tricks an set trapcannons with salt he coulden catch them till…. but lemme tell yo the story so you kin see an know wa we mean by 'till' because if a go on t'ain gon bi no need a telling you about how he catch the thieves.

Ole Jo Samuel had a big piece a land dung in the Bottom somewhere between the Bay a Biskay an One Hoe and he use to plant sea island cotton on it. He had a house up on Bishop Hill where he could look dung over he land and could see if the pickin was going on right an if the men an womin he had workin for him wassen loitering away they time talkin an jokin. If he saw tha they wasn't workin or if it was time to stop for the day he'd blow on a conchshell so the pickers ud know he was lookin or that was time to knock off.

He had an overseer who was a good man and who had been workin for him for more than ten years. He name was Jim. Now Jim had one fault, tho he was stronger and bigger than any of them, an could work hard and stand the heat better than any body he had one fault. Any time a the day or the night he would get lickerd up an the only thing he could do when he was drunk was to go to sleep just where he was and sometimes he could drink so much tha he'd be sleeping for days. Ole Jo had a liking for Jim and tha is why he did'n lose he job, an because the pickers did'n work hard when Jim was drunk an sleeping somewhere ole Jo had to keep he eye on them an use he conchshell if they was'n going about they work as they should.

One morning Jim come running up to the house an started calling: "*Mister Johannes, Mister Johannes……*".

Ole Jo called out: "*Wha ye want Jim*".

"*The thieves Mister Johannes, the sons of a ….. a beg yo pardon Mister*

Johannes, but they been thieves in the cotton field last night an they nearly clean out the place we started with yesterday afternoon. Thieves Mister Johannes, thieves the sons of a ..... a beg ye pardon Mister Johannes".

"Wha yo sain Jim? A don suppose you bin drinkin agin?"

"No Mister Johannes a aint had a drop since night before last. A speaking the truth Mister Johannes they's been thieves in the cotton field last night an they pick about fo barrels a cotton an right a the best kind too."

"Jim if you certain it happen like you say we gon have to do something to stop them, because if they succeed once they gon try again. Now listen to me you gon have to stay sober today and not work too hard so you can watch for the thieves tonight. But you musn't tell nobody."

*"All right Mister Johannes a gon try to catch
them tonight an a gon watch real good."*

So tha night Jim watched fo the thieves and walked up and down the plantation but he did not see or hear nothing because the thieves did'n come tha night an the night after tha they didn come either. On the third nite when Jim was walking dung the road to take up he watch, he saw a bottle lying in the middle a the road an he picked it up. When he opened the bottle he find it was full a strong rum.

*"A suppose somebody must a lose it, a better
take it along before somebody else find it."*

So Jim took up he watch with the bottle a rum under he arm, and after he had walked around a bit he sat dung to wait. But afterall he had been watching for 2 nites he was tired an he said to heself: *"They'nt thieves coming tonite, they fraid a me so a might just as well take a drink."*

So Jim took a drink from the bottle and after a while another.

And in a jiffy the bottle was empty an in a short while Jim was snoring away and dreaming about catching the cotton thieves.

But when Jim woke up the nex morning the thieves had steal another four barrels of cotton an Jim had to go up an tell Ole Johannes that he had been sleepin while the thieves picked the cotton.

When Ole Johannes hear this he said: *"A got to catch thim, an a can let you watch no more because you gon get drunk again and let them get away. A gon set salt cannons. Jim, get me the cannons outta the cellar, we gon set them tonite after dark."*

And that nite Jim and Ole Jo set the cannons in the cotton fields an run the wires all through the fields so that as soon as anybody touch the wires the cannons would go off and wake up the people on Bishop Hill so they could run dung to try an catch the thieves they could get away. They loaded the cannons with gunpowder and coarse salt so that if somebody was in fronta the cannon when it went off he'd get a load a salt under he skin; an he'd be afraid to go stealin again because it wud give him lots a pain to get the salt out befor it had start to melt in he blood.

But the thieves were smart, they picked the
cotton without touchin a wire an when they had enough they pulled one a the wires an ran away. When Ole Jim hear the cannons go off he jumped outta bed an ran dung the hill to the Bottom with some a the servants, in they nitegungs with clubs and machetes in they hands but they coulden find a soul in the whole cotton field. So Jim an Ole Johannes with all they tricks and traps coulden catch the thieves an Ole Jo loss a lotta cotton.

An they woulda never caught the thieves if one nite after dark, three donkeys that Ole Jo use to use to pull he carts an carry he bags a cotton to the gin, if these three donkeys hadden jump outta the grasspiece where they use to stay an got into the cottonfields.

Tha nite when the thieves come to steal they didn see the donkeys, but in the dark one a the men butt up against a donkey an this one lashed out an give this fellow a brace a kicks so hard that he started to bawl; He friends run up to help him, but in the dark they too ran up against the donkeys and they got kicked an trampled an the louder they bawled the louder the donkeys brayed and the harder they kicked. All this commotion in the middle a the nite woke up Ole Johannes and he got he servants outta bed and they run dung to the cotton field from which the noise was coming an after they had calm dung the donkeys, the found the thieves on the grung groaning and bawling nearly kicked to death by the animals crying out: *"Hold ye watchdogs…. Don't let them go on us again…. We'en gone steal no mo from ye Mister Johannes. Hold ye devils…don't let them get at us again."* Jim and the servants picked up the thieves an took them up to the house an lock them up in a cellar.

Now tha's how Ole Jo Samuel get rid a men who was stealing he cotton. An now a suppose ye know wha a mean when a said 'till….'. The meanin was… till the donkeys broke loose, because if the donkeys hadden break outta they pasture Jim and Ole Johannes woulda never catch the thieves.

Goodnight folks,

Jim and Anna

Breakfast April 15, 1950

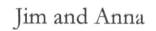

Ayo remember Jim who use to work for Ole Mister Jo?

Some weeks ago a tole you the story about Mr. Johannes an the cotton thieves an how he an he overseer with all they tricks coulden catch the thieves. Now this overseer tha is the Jim a mean. Wha he other name is a don know and a suppose nobody else know either, because he was always called Jim.

After Jim had work for Mister Johannes for ten long years Jo give im a lil piece a land dung by One Hoe and Jim marry Anna, one a the servants from up Bishop Hill, who had come over from Anguilla when she was a lil girl, to play with Jo's daughter.

Anna had been one a Mrs. Samuels best cooks and she use to bake the sweetest titty-bread and the best bread-pudding in the island. Whenever there was a feast up on the Hill she would be maken cakes and niceties for days and days.

On this piece of land Jim build he cowdung kingdom outta watlin an posts. Mister Jo let him cut up in Rice Hill an from cowdung he had dig outta the cowpen a Mister Johannes. Jim put good thatch on the roof an white wash the walls so the house was pretty to look at.

After tha was done he pick up all the rocks in the yard an build a wall round the place, plant some flowers side the house an put in he furniture. An Jim an Anna went to live in they new house.

Jim keep on working for Mister Jo but he wassen no more overseer, now an then he'd do a odd job when Mister Johannes was a hand short, an Anna still use to help in the kitchen up Bishop Hill.

Jim and Anna had buy a goat an because they wassen home all day to keep a eye on it, it had to stay tie fast when they was out working. But sometimes the goat would bust she rope or pull out the stake, jump the wall, go dung to the Quarter and run dung people walls or eat up they potatoes in they grungs. And when they had goat kids and the kids started to eat up an trample the yam an tania grungs, Jim an Anna had to pay a lotta pound money an damages to get they property outta pound and because the pound master didden like Jim it use to take Jim a lotta he time looking for he goat an the kids.

One day when Jim was walking back from the pound-yard leading he two goat kids along he was thinking of the trouble the kids had cost again today:

"*If it wassen for Anna I'd sell these good for nothing things long ago an a would live in peace. Yes, an tha son of a pound master. He give me another fine again, an only after he had see me pass the third time he called out to aks if a was looking for me goat again while he had them in the pound-yard all along. Tha was the second time this week an after they get bigger these kids ain't gon know no better than tha they can trespass an run dung people walls the whole day an cost me a lotta worry an money.*"

When he got home he tie the kids fast just like they mother, with a piece of rope just long enough for them to walk around and fed. So Jim keep he goats tie out an as long as they didden get away he had peace an rest an he an Anna could work for Mister Jo an other people.

In a short time they had five big goats, Anna use to milk the she ones so they didden have to buy milk from somebody else, an they was even talking about butchering a goat with Xmas an selling part a the meat to buy a pig an cornin the other part in pickle to keep.

And Jim an Anna would say: "*If we buy a lil pig we could butcher it nex year an eat an sell a lotta pork an a like pork better than goat meat, we can make sauce an saucages. It will be easy to feed it, because a pig eat everything that you throw away. An this ain gon cause no trouble at all by getting in people grungs, it can get outta the yard by jumping the walls.*"

Capin Johnson and the lil red snapper

Broadcast May 20, 1950

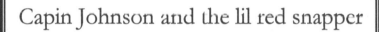

Over by Oyster Pond use to be a lil one room shack. Ole Capin Johnson use to live there. This shack had been a boathouse whe the fishermen use to keep they boats. Capin Johnson had patch it up with pieces a ole kerosene pans he had find on the bayside where they had washed ashore.

Capin Johnson had been first mate for years on a three master tha use to sail between the islands with salt, and he had load a lotta sugar from San Domingo an cotton from Statia an St. Maartenn for the States. Later he had become capin on the Santa Fe, a schooner tha had the reputation that she could out sail anything on the seven seas.

He had sailed for mo than 30 years from island to island carrying all kind a cargo, cattle an sheep, dung an salt, and all such things tha people could use. He had even carried a couple loads a rum to the States an he had never meet up with any trouble with the customs because they could never catch him. He was a real ole weather beaten salt and because he was a good weather prophet he had always been able to get he ship laid up in a good harbor before a hurricane could catch up with him. The only narrow escape he had at sea was when the compass on the Santa Fe had gone wrong on him and he had end up a trip to Macoris somewhere dung by South America.

When he had settle dung ole man Johnson had take up living over by Oyster Pond, where he had use to lay up he ship in the hurricane months and where he could live a quiet life with the sea near to hand, talk to the fishermen about the weather, fishing an boats, an exchange stories with the men a the ships that still use to come in to lay up in the pond.

The inside a he shack he had made to look just like he dogcabin on board and he use to feel at home sittin in he ole chair smoking he pipe an lookin at the walls tha was decorated with charts, compasses, an barometers, with pictures a all kinds a ships an sorts a junk he had pick up on trips.

The capin had a lil dory he use to go out in to set he fish pots or try to hook fish. When he'd catch too much for he self he'd either corn them or go to tung with them or sell them along the road to buy cornmeal, tobacco an rum.

One day he even catch a turtle when it was laying eggs in the sand. It was a big one and he find the nest with 30 fresh eggs. For days and days he was eatin nothing but turtle soup, turtle stew and boiled turtle eggs.

He had a friend [capin Simson], who still use to sail and who use to come an look him up whenever he was in Great Bay and sometimes. Capin Simson, who didden have any family like ole Johnson, use to lay up in Oyster Pond to wait for the sun to cross the line an so bring the hurricane months to a end. Then Johnson would have some fine days chattin about ole times, about fast ships and slow ones and about all the harbours they had seen together and alone.

One morning Capin Johnson rowed out in he dory to see wha he had in he fish pots. He hadden catch no fish for a few days an this morning he was hopin to find a good pot. But after he find he markers an pulled up his pots he find them nearly empty again with nothing eatable inside.

"*Ah wonder how tha come*" he said to heself "*for days an days a can't catch enough to eat an a can stand eatin cornmeal without fish.*"

So Johnson rowed he dory home, walk over to he shack for a couple o fishing lines and went out in he boat again to try he luck with small fry as bait. After he had anchored the dory he put fries on he hooks an set out two lines, one on either side a the boat. After he had been waitin for a good while he said to he self: "*Ah suppose all the blaireyes must be hidden and they aint a grunt or yellowtail nowhere near.*"

So he waited and talked to he self about the ole wifes an doctors he use to catch an about the time the kingfish had come on he small line. *"Yeah"*, he said, *"those us to be me good days a suppose a must be getting old. Now a gon have to eat dry cornmeal again tonight."* An he started to pull up he lines.

When he first line was nearly in he felt a jerk and bawling out *"a got him, a got him"*, he pulled faster. When he get he hook outta the water he find a small red snapper on it so small that when he take it up to take out the hook he could hold im in the palm a he hand.

"Please mister fisherman a ain do you nothing" the red snapper called out *"please throw me back, a too small for you to eat."*

"Tha is true" the capin said, *" but you the first fish a see in 3 days an a can't stand eatin dry cornmeal. Now a got you, even if 1 had to hookja through you tail when a was pulling in me lines."*

"Throw me back mister fisherman an you gon see tha ye luck gon change. A gon lead a lotta fish to ye lines and fishpots, and a gon do it every day for you once you throw me back. An you gon catch more fish than you ever did in ye life."

"Allright, allright a gon do it" capin Johnson said an so he take he hook outta the tail a the red snapper an throw him overboard.

In the next five minutes a waitin capin Johnson keep on cussin he self for a soft hearted fool: *"Now a had a fish an a had to go an throw it away. It was a fish even if it was a small one. An a suppose the lil thing must be laughing at me dung there."*

But all at once he got a strike on he left-hand-line, an he just pulled in a big grunt when he got a strike on he other line.... An so it keep on for hours, no sooner than he had pulled up one line with fish he got a strike on the other. When he had catch about fifty fish he was tired out, so he pulled in he lines an went home with he dory loaden dung with fish. When he got to he shack he find capin Simson waiting for him an before he reached the shore he started to call out: *"Man ye should see the heap a fish a catch, come help me get them outta the boat."* Then capin Johnson told he friend all tha had happened while he was fishing.

"Ayo looka trouble you ain't been drinkin a hope", Simson said, *"or maybe ye got a sunstroke from the hot weather...."*

"Man a tellin the truth but if ye don believe me, come jump in the boat and lets go out to see if me pots got anything in them."

So they pulled out to the place where he had set he pots an while Johnson steadied the dory, Simson pulled up a pot. It was so heavy with fish he could hardly hold it. When at last he got the pot over the side a the boat, both a the ole men sat dung with they eyes poppin outta they heads lookin at the fishpot. This was so full a fish that capin Simson had to say: *"A aint had a drink for the whole day otherwise I'd say a was drunk, but now a gotta believe me own eyes an a suppose the story ye tole me was true."*

Tha is the way the lil red snapper keep he promise to capin Johnson and the capin always had all the fish he wanted to eat and lots to sell to boot.

Sharks in Lamejo

Broadcast June 25, 1950

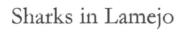

A was walkin dung the yardhill, thinkin about the drought an tha if we didden get rain soon all the grass trees would burn up an all the cattle an sheep would die. We hadden had no rain since February an now it was August, all the slobs was dry out a long time ago, an only the best wells still gave water.

When a come to the gate leading dung to the salt ponds, a hear somebody call out: "*Johnny, Johnny, wait a minute*". So a walk up to the gate and there a see Daniel coming running from rung the pond.

When he reach me he said outta breath: "*They in the bay again Johnny, they in the bay again*".

"*Who in the bay again, Danny? Calm dung man an don try to talk so fast.*"

"*Oh Johnny, the sharks. A just come up from Lamejo bay. A was dung there trying me luck with a fishline when a see them. They at least twenty a them an some big ones too...*"

"*Come less go dung an have a look at them*", a said. And so we walk the road through the gate; we pass the ponds where they was pickin salt, an pass to big salt heaps, and after we had pass the fringe grape-trees we come out on the bayside. The blarin sun made it hard on the eyes to look out across the water an the heat beatin at you from the sand was awfull.

"*They up by the rock, near the point on the left hand side a the bay*", Danny said. So we walk dung there, I forgetting a didden have on me ole shoes, over the rocks on broken conqshells. When we got out half way the point Danny said: "*Look the they be. Two, three, fo, a see about nine big ones an some small ones.*"

An lookin dung in the water, some ten feet from the shore a could see the sharks together lying still in the water with only they tails movin from one side to the other.

After we had watch them fo a while Danny said: "*come less go tell Jojo*". So we walk up to the Quarter an on the way Danny tell how they had catch a lotta sharks last year an about the new shark net Jojo was makin because he ole one had been bust last year when he had round up too much sharks at a time: "*But you gon see tha this time this one ain gon bust… Look, Jojo got he net out behind he house, he must be workin on it now.*"

We walk through a gap in the wall an rung the house and the we find Jojo makin the last knots in he net.

"*Hello Johnny. Wha Danny a thought you was dung Lamejo Bay fishing, wha bring you up here this time a the day?*"

"*The sharks Jojo*", Danny said, "*they come in this morning an they some big ones with them too. A was dung there fishin but when a see them a run up to tell you. They come in sooner this year, but a suppose they must be more comin, because we only see about fifteen. When you gon try yo net at them Jojo?*"

"*Now lemme see, a gon need another day to make the floates on me net. An then a got to go Great Bay to get some mo rope,….. less try our luck on Saturday. Danny you must warn the boys who help us last year. They know wha to do an a don want to bust me new net on the first try.*"

So we waited a few days while Jojo finished he net and Danny, meself an some a the other Quarter boys would walk dung to look at the sharks in the bay, an every day we could count some mo swimming up an dong the bay.

On Saturday morning Jojo load he net on a ole cart an he an Danny shobbed it dung to the beach, while the other boys an meself took the ropes to the bay. First Jojo an Danny went out in a rowboat to have a look at the sharks tha was swimmin up an dung the bay from one side to the other, to see if they wassen excited.

Then they made fast one end a the net to a post on the shore, load the rest in the boat an while Danny rowed out in the bay playin out the net behind him, Jojo swam out in front a the boat with the other end. When they had get about halfway the bay the sharks started to pass on they way to the right hand side of the bay. Jojo an Danny waited till the big bunch had pass, then Jojo went on swimming an with the en a the net in he hand he went rung two sharks tha was straglin along behind the rest.

Danny played out the rest a the net as fast as he could an rowin with all he might he made for the shore picking up Jojo with the end a the net as he pass him, They jump outta the [boat] as soon as they reach the shore, an the other men rushed up to help them.

Up to then the fish hadden notice tha they was in a net, but when the men started to pull in the net on both sides, the sharks started to rush at the net trying to get [out] an jumpin an turnin rushed from one side to the other, but Jojo had make he net good and strong. The nearer the sharks got to the shore, the more the water boiled with the lashing out a they tails, but it didden help any. The men pulled the struglin fishes up on the beach an Jojo slipped a rope rung they tails an they pulled them outta the net.

"Phew....,tha was a warm job, one moment a thought they was goin to bust the net again. Tha big one must be a least a ten footer, wha you say Johnny", Danny asked me.

"A don know how big he is, but a sure glad he can chase me no mo."

Meanwhile Jojo was over haulin he net on one a the boats after the sharks had been cut open, take out the liver to make sharkoil, an Danny take up the pilot-fishes that come ashore with the sharks.

The people who had come dung to see the excitement left the beach, we put the net an ropes on the cart an went home.

The dead sharks started to stink in the bleachin sun, the others in the water still swimming up and dung the bay from one side to the other.

Hurricane!

Broadcast September 16, 1950

It was a long time ago tha the islands had they last bad hurricane but now nearly at the end of the season Sint Maarten has been struck by one tha was worse than any they had before, a gon tell ye a story about one. But you must remember it's a story an a don know if 't happen for true.

It had been a hot an dry year, all through June and July the sun had burn up all the grass an had dry out all the slobs an waterholes. An even the springs rung the ponds scarcely gave any water. All the people lose a lot a cattle an sheep an all the cattle tha was still living was only skin over bones and they could hardly walk to find food.

In August the weather had started off hotter than ever an even the people could scarcely stand the heat. Durin the hottest hours of the day everybody would get in the shade an lie dung because if they worked in the sun they"d get a sunstroke or would faint. During the night the people would sleep with all the winders an doors open an some would even make they beds up outside on the gallery

One afternoon ole Sammy was sittin dung in a rocker on he gallery talkin to he friend Jacky Jones: *"No Jacky, a don like this weather atall, something gon happen soon, a don like the colour a the sky, an this hot weather can mean nothing good."*

"A don like it either Sammy, tha yellow colour in the sky mean we gon get a change a wheather; a remember ten years ago we had about the same kind a weather, an tha ended in a hurricane. A don like it atall, a don..... say Sammy, look who comin in the gate. A wonder what ye done now."

"Wha Jack, you know a always been a law-abidin man an a really don know wha a policeman gon have to see me for. A ain don nuthen tha could make them in tung send a pliesman out to me. But maybe he lookin for you."

By now the policeman had reach the gallery: *"Good afternoon gentlemen; Message from the governor: a hurricane gon reach us about seven*

119

o'clock tonight, you must see that everything is in good shape before that time, warn everybody else you see. Good day gentlemen."

All during these words the men was listening with they mouth open with surprise written all over they faces. When the policeman had finished they caught they breath and called out to him goodbye an thanks.

Then Jacky said: "A tole you a didden like the looks a the sky. But a got hurry home an get things ready. As soon as the gale is over a gon come over to see how you get throu it all. So long Sammy."

"So long Jacky.... see that you bar up all ye windows good."

Johnson left an Sammy went into the house to tell he wife Leonteen the news.

"Leonteen, you put the cows in the pen an put you coalpots, an pans an everything else inside outta the way, oh yes, an don't forget the fowls and the dogs. A gon get the horse an after tha a gon bar up the windows."

Both a them started out to get the work done. After Sammy put the horse away in he stable with he drinkbucket full a water an some hay for him to eat, he started out to bar up the house, closing all the bolts on the inside an after tha was finished, he got he hammer an a pocketful a nails an nailed the doors an windows shut from the outside. Then he climbed up on the roof an nailed dung all the loose shingles he could find.

In the meantime the yellow light in the sky had become deeper and deeper and was nearly orange. The sun was still shining but it coulden change the colouring in the sky, everything looked like you was looking throu dark orange glasses.

Sammy stood on the roof looking rung a few minutes. Everything was pretty to look at, an there wassen no wind at all but still it was a frightening sight, it make you feel small an powerless. Quickly for a old man Sammy got dung off he roof an went to help he wife.

When everything was ready they went into the house to eat sumpen an to see if everything inside was allright.

After a while Sammy went outside to look about. The first pufs a wind started to come an because everything was so dry a lotta dust was blowing about. So Sammy went back inside and closed and bolted the do.

"In another hour we gon be right in the middle of it", he said to he wife *"an a sure hope the ole house can stand the strain"*.

They sat dung an waited. Meantime the gusts a wind become stronger and stronger and they keep on comin faster and faster, the noise got so loud that even inside they had to call out loud to make theyselves understood.

The ole house was groaning an creakin all the time an now an then they'd hear sompthing hit the house with a bang.

With a loud roar it started to thunder an the lightening was so bright tha they could see it light up the whole place throu the cracks in the windows an at the same time the rain started to fall on the roof, louder and louder the noise got, with the wind howlin, the house groanin, the thunder rumbling an the rain hittin the building like shot.

They lose track a time and altho it was very late they couden go to sleep. They just sat dung and listened, for the noise was so loud that with bawlin out they could scarecely hear wha was said. After about four hours the wind started to die dung a bit an the thunder stopped, but it kep on rainin as hard as ever.

"*A hope the cattle don get drung, but the worst must be over now so we might just as wel go to bed now, an you can't go outside or see anything.*" Sammy said.

The nex morning both were up early an everything was quiet. They opened the door an went outside. The yard was full a branches, shingles an all kinds a broken up material, the gate was blown dung an a lot a shingles was off the roof. Two a the big trees back a the house was blown dung an the rest didden have a leaf on them.

"*Look at the big holes the water make in the grung*", Leonteen called out "*...an all me rose trees broken to pieces.*"

Later in the day, after Sammy had clean up the rubbish an find tha two a he fowls was dead, he sat on he gallery talkin to Jack.

"*Wha Sammy, a think tis a good thing we only got the tail end otherwise they'd abeen much mo damage. Now as far as a hear in tung nobody been killed, but some houses were mashed to pieces, a steamer run ashore in Great Bay, how she got over the bar nobody can tell; an a few schooners was broken to pieces on the shore. A sure think we got off good this time.*"

"*Yea Jacky, tha is wha oi think too, but a suppose the po debbels tha got the full force a the gale didden get so good. Yea... we sho must be thankful we got off so good this time.*"

The poisen covalley

Broadcast October 14, 1950

"Wha hello Loysie – Yo just the person a was looking for. Wha yo got to do this afternoon?"

"Wha Johnny, yo know a sin, got nothing to do this afternoon, otherwise yo wooden a meet me sittin here this time a the day. But why yo want to know wha a got to do. A hope yo don wan me to go over to Marigot with yo?"

"No man. Yo remember tha a promise yo to take you out fishin with me one a these days? Wha yo think about goin with us this afternoon to try an round up some jacks, we goin with three boats an a need one more man for my boat…..an as a promise to take yo with me…. But if yo don wan togo, a can get Fredric."

"Ayo looka trouble, Johnny yo know a goin with yo an yo mussen try to stop me, a gon have to go home fust to put on a ole pants. Wha time we leavin an who goin in the boat with us, an who gon be in the other boats."

An while they talked, Loysie aksin questions an Johnny anserin them, they walked up the street.

Loysie had been sittin dung in fronta the boathouse by the wharf lookin out over the sea where yo could see Saba in the distance lookin just like a big felt hat comin outta the water. *"A suppose tha from over there we mus look like some kinda new fangled hat or the other"*, Loysie had thought.

Near the end of the wharf a lot a lil boys was swimming arung in the water with they arms shining in the sun every time they made a stroke. Now an then one a the ones tha wanted to show off fer the others, would run up the steps a the wharf, get up on the front railin and dive dung with a big shout right in the middle a the others.

"A wish oi could go out there an amuse meself like they. Look at them swimming about just like big brown fishes an happy as can be." These was wha Loysie was thinkin when Johnny found him dreamin an lookin out at the picture in front of him.

125

When the three boats was ready an all men had come up, they shoved off an hoisted they sails. With a good wind in the sails they moved outta the bay an over the bar. Loysie was sittin dung near the back a the boat an because it was the fust time he had ever crossed the bar he keep lookin dung to see when they was across.

"Look at the houses yo can scarcely make out which is which, and the wharf look just like a lil step. Wha, we pass Pointe Blanche already an Saba still look just as big as from the wharf. The water must be good deep here….". All these things passed throu he thoughts but he didden say anything because he didden want the other men to laugh at him.

When they was a couple miles off the Point, the Lady Jennings passed them goin in, an just after tha they catch up with the boat tha was in front an was now waitin for them.

It was Tom Peterson boat an he called out to the other boats: *"Come on, make it snappy. Ayo always got to be late, an if yo don hurry now all the jacks gon be gone. Wha yo think they waitin for yo to catch them?"*

"Yo know Loysie", Johnny said, *"everytime we got out together Tom keeps remindin us tha his boat is faster than ours, but one a these days a gon build a faster boat an then we can see who gon laugh. But come we got to work now an hurry too. Look Loysie…. The jacks. Over there where yo see all those pelikins."*

Meanwhile the three boats had come up close together an it was decided tha when Tom and Johnny played out the net between they two boats the other one would go rung an start to chase the jacks up. An soon the thing was done, when the net was ready between the boats, the boats sailed forward an at the same time they sailed the net in a half circle up to where the pelikins was circling aroun an divin dung one after the other. The two boats with the net sailed so tha they made the circle tighter an tighter while the men in the other boat beat the water with sticks an oars.

"Good so boys, we got them. Pull the net me boys, we got them…"

When they had finished pullin in the net they had both the boats with a good load in them; they put some a the jacks in the third boat and with a good wind in the sails they made for the harbor.

As they got near the bayside, the men up in front a the boat started to come up to get they jacks for the supper. All the men had they hands full countin out jacks for the buyers an getting out change. After all the fish was gone the men washed out the boats and pulled them right up on the bayside.

Loysie walked up the bayside with Johnny, both with a strap of jacks in they hand. *"Man tha was a nice trip"*, Loysie said, *"yo can get me to go out with yo any time yo want, once a don have to work."*

"How about goin out with me tomorrow morning early, a got some pots set out near the Bluff an a want to look at them early. We can row out an get back before 8 o'clock, how about it, yo goin?"

"Of course a goin."

An so bright an early morning find the two a them out in the [boat] rowin from one fishpot to the other. Th fust pot tha they pulled up only had in a few dead fish, a shellfish an a conger.

"Tha good fo nothing thing gone an eat up or kill all the fish, a sure yon lun him to play a trick like tha on me". An saying tha he chop the conger head with one blow a the ole machete he had in the boat.

The other pots had in a good catch: grunts, blaireyes, yellowtails, olewives an a few shellfish.

"Now the last one", Johnny said. An while Loysie steadied the boat he pulled the pot up. *"Man she heavy like the dikes, a bet yo this the*

best catch for the morning, an it sure look like yo gon bring me luck..... Ayo looka work, what ha be Loysie, look at tha....”

"They only one fish in the pot Johnny, but tis a big one tha must weigh at least 30 pungs, wha kinda fish tha kin be Loysie?”

"Man tha's tha biggest blaireye-covalley a ever see, if you want to eat him yo can have him... Oi don want him, a can feel the itch already.”

"Wha yo mean by tha?”

"Man, most a these covalleys poisen, an this one sure must be otherwise heddanever get to be so big...a sure feel the itch already. No suh, oi ain gon eat him.”

"Throw him in the boat to show when we get ashore, but oi don want him either.”

When the get ashore they strap up the fish an when Johnny see Sue Duncan walkin dung bayside, he called out to her to come see wha he had catch.

"Now yo got a big lot the Johnny”, Sue said. *"Wha yo gon do with tha covalley? A never see one tha was so big.”*

"Wha a only brought it in to show aroun, after tha a gon throw it away, nobody gon want tha.”

"Give it to me, oi can use it...”, an takin the covalley up she walked off.

"Ayo, tha fish sure gon make her sick. But tha her nag o trouble.”

A couple days later Loysie meet Sue walkin up the street.

"Hello Sue, a hope the covalley didden hurt yo.”

"It didden hurt me at all. When a come home a cut off a lil piece an give it to Miss Eunice cat tha was in me backyard, an the whole morning a watched the cat an tha didden get sick, so as a didden see why oi should get sick a eat a nice piece an corn the rest."

Simple Island justice

Broadcast March 17, 1951

Hello folks, tonite a gon tell you a story somebody from home wrote me about, an a hope he is listenin tonight.

This is a story tha happened years gon by when Mister Johannes use to plant cotton an cane on Belvedère an Belplaine an a suppose some a the ole people can remember those days.

Up to some years ago you could see the chimney a the plant dung Belplaine but now it been pull dung, anyhow it use to be where Chick-Chick got he house now. In those days all the flat land a Belplaine an Belvedère was planted with sugarcane an there was cane fields everywhere you looked.

Some time ago a tole ayo about the feller who use to steal Mister Johannes cotton. Now they was another fellow who was very bad character, he name was Joseph, but everybody call him Mooner Joseph. How he got tha name nobody ever knew, nut tha is wha he was called, an he answered to the name.

Now Mooner was a good thief, an when as say good a mean he could steal without bein caught. Whenever the canes was ripe in Mister Joe's fiels Joseph was sure to get he part before all the cane could be reaped. Mister Johannes had to hire extra men to guard the cane field an altho he overseer Jim did he best and stayed up nights on a stretch, the men couden catch Mooner. A couple of times they would pen Joseph up but even with a bunch a canes in he arms he could outrun all the men, an so he got away every time.

But one night when he was running away from the guards he tripped over a wire Jim had stretch out in the cane field fo tha purpose and before Joseph could scramble to he feet three a the men who was chasin him jumped on top of him an started to beat him up.

When Jim come up to the men he said: *"Come less take him up to Mister Johannes to see wha he gon do to this thief."*

So they walked Mooner up to Belvedère, an when Mister Joe hear the commotion in the yard he get outta he bed an putting he head outta the window he called out: *"Hey Jim, what the dickens happenin dung there…".*

"We got him Mister Johannes, we got the thief. And tis Mooner just like we say it would be."

"Bring him up the gallery", Mister Joe called.

The men took Joseph up to the gallery and waited till Mister Johannes came out with a lamp in he hand. He handed the lamp to Jim and stood [sain] Mooner: *"So we got you at last, a hope you get punished so you don't ever feel like stealin cane again."*

"Wha Mister Johannes", Jim said, *"you mussen turn him over to the law right away, let the men give him a good beatin first, they had started to do so already but a stopped them because a thought you would know a better way to punish him. They gon only put him in jail, when he out he gon have a lot trouble to catch him, he can run faster than any of us."*

"Tha's true wha you say Jim, a wonder if he can really run fast…..".

Mister Joe stood thinkin for a few moments then he said: *"A know wha a gon do. Come take Joseph dung to [back of the] house an Jim, give the lamp to one a the others an go get Nelson."*

Nero was part bulldog and part bloodhound, and tha was the dog Mister Joe use to use to catch goats tha would jump he walls and come into the canefields. An Nelson a real killer. Once he got a throat hold, a goat would never get away.

Standing behind the house Mister Joe said to Mooner: *"You can choose, which you prefer, either a turn yo over to the law in tung so they can put you in jail, or a turn you loose an set this dog on you. If you can outrun the dog you free, if you don't you gon be the one tha gon be in trouble. A don't believe*

134

you can run so fast at all."

Mooner Joseph was always proud he could outrun everybody an he didden want to land in jail so he said: *"A run better than your old dog any day. Just turn me loose an a gon show you."*

"A thought you was fool enough to try it", Mister Joe said, *"turn him loose men an loosen the dog at the same time"*.

An so it happened, when both were loose the man and the dog stood watching each other, then suddenly Joseph turn an at tha moment Jim called out *"Get him Nelson"* and the dog set out barkin after Mooner.

But to the surprise a all the men, the man reached the mill – rung an in two jumps was across it, an was tearin throu the bush with the dog running barking behind him.

How Joseph got away from Nelson nobody know, some people say he musta climbed a tree, another say he outrun the dog. If you go dung Bethlehem you can sometimes hear the dog up Belvedère still barking at Joseph.

When Joseph was a small boy he had started stealin an he give he father an mother, who was law-abidin people – lots of trouble. He father nearly wear out heself beatin Joseph but nothin could stop him.

One day after he father had taken some cane from him tha Joseph had stolen from Mister Jo he father said: *"We got to get rid a the boy, he gon be a big disgrace for the family if we don give him a good punishment."*

So he father barreled Joseph up and let the barrel down [the hill where it] struck busted open. Joseph crawled outta the staves an called out to he father, who was standin up the hill.

"A goin right back in Mister Romondt cane piece".

So you see, nothing could keep Joseph from stealin.

Good nite folks.

Rumrunners'plight

Broadcast July 17, 1951

It was a coal evening in August an after the blazing hot day the people were sitting dung on they galleries enjoying the cool breeze, or walkin arong for a little exercise, which they hadden been able to take during the day on account of the heat. Every now and then you'd hear: *"Good evening Ma'm…. Good evening Mister so and so"*, as somebody passed a gallery with people on it, or when acquaintances met in the street.

"Nice evening Joe."

"Fine weather Jack, but it gon be hot again tomorrow".

"Ayo, the breeze is a lot cooler than last night."

Everybody was speakin bout the nice weather, an where you had scarcely seen a soul on the street the whole day, nobody who could manage it stayed inside now that it was better to be outside than indoors. Here and there you could hear a child crying, because it was too hot to sleep. A lotta young folks was walkin along the bayside, or standing in groups together talkin and laughin.

Capen Johannes had walk dung the street after coming ashore from board he schooner. Everywhere he met people he knew an he'd stop an chat a bit with them.

"Come up on the gallery capen", Sam Johnson called out. *"Come up on the gallery and rest your legs. We gon have a cool drink."* Sam walked to the door and called out: *"Mary, a got capen Johnson out here, bring some cold drinks."*

Capen Johnson sat dung on the gallery: *"How are you all getting on here? A see you been having a lotta hot weather."*

"O, everybody here getting on alright, an life is still the same. Not much news around here. But how was your trip, let's hear how you made out this time."

"Hello Mary", capen Johnson said, *"thanks a lot. Now my trip was good, although I had some bad weather we got through alright. Tha is better luck than the Yank rum smuggler had."*

"Which one you mean", Sam asked, sipping he drink, *"is it the one who been in Marigot lately?"*.

"Yes, it is the schooner Amelia, she been in Marigot a couple times."

[Text missing]

"......were dead on their feet. The poor fellows who had faced death a thousand times in the past two days were brought aboard and fed, but the capen, a good sailor refused to leave his ship, he just lay dung on her deck an went to sleep. From the mate I got the rest sad story: For two days an night nobody had got a wink a sleep. They had tied theyselves together to keep from being washed overboard. And pumping away they had saved they lives, the ship or what was left of her and they cargo. Somehow the water in her hold hadden risen beyond a certain point an so the good schooner had managed to keep afloat. We towed the ship to the nearest harbor, back the same way we had just come. We put the men ashore and that was tha. They sure was lucky we came along when we did. The men wooden a held out pumpin much longer."

"Capen, come, we'll umpty our glasses to their luck and drink another to yours."

After finishing the last drink capen Johannes said: *"Come a must be getting back aboard. We got a lot to do tomorrow morning an a gon be leavin for Statia in the evening. Good night Sam, my regards to you Mary good night, and thanks a lot."*

The capen walked up the street, which was a lot quieter than when he came ashore. Sam Johnson and he wife sat for a while on the gallery with they face in the evening breeze. Then they turned in after saying goodnight to their neighbours across the street. In a short while everything outside was quiet with only the rushing a the wind in the trees or a shutter rattling to break the silence.

Sint Maarten

Broadcast November 10, 1951

Hello folks, tonite a got a story especially for you Sint Martiners where ever you are. It's about the saint after who our island was named and about how they keep his nameday over here 'Sintermaarten'.

In long years gone by, it was around the year 350, Martin was a soldier in the roman army an he was stationed in France. One day when he was leaving the city of Tours he passed a poor beggar who was sitting near the gates waiting for alms.

An as Martin was a poor soldier without money he didden have anything to give the beggar. But because he saw that the poor man was blue an shivering with cold, he took off he thick soldiers coat an drawing he sword he cut the cloak in two an gave one half to the poor beggar.

Sint Maarten is a well-known saint in Holland. A Lotta children are named after him, towers or churches in Groningen, Middelburg, Venlo, Maastricht, Utrecht remind us of him an in places like Maartensdijk here near Hilversum, Sint Maarten in North Holland and Sint Maartenshoek in Zeeland we find the name.

Anyhow tomorrow is Sint Maartens day an this day is a feast for the children. For that day they have been getting their things ready for the evening of the 11th of November. The children are thinking of the hollow pumpkins in which they have put a piece of candle.

They are thinking of all the sweets an fruit they gon get, an some are lookin on while they father or mother are fixing up a jack'o lantern for them.

In Limburg Sint Maarten fires are lit in the evening an it is a fine sight to see the fires flaring up on the hill along the Meuse going from village to village. The children light their own torches

[from] the bonfire an go strolling with their torches held high over their heads while they keep singin in their Limburg dialect:

[Intermission with music:

Sinter Mertes veugelke,
haet ein roëd wit keugelke.
Haet ein blauw stertje,
Van je hoepsa Sinter Merte.
Vandaag is 't Sinter Merte,
morrege Sinter Krökke.
Dan kòmme die gooje herte,
die hadde zo gaer ein stökske.
Hauw maar op körrefke,
Sinter Mertes körrefke.
Hölt, hölt, hölt,
en 's winters is 't kald.
Hoera, hoera, waat hebbe de boere ein laeve,
hoera, hoera, waat hebbe de boere ein pret[xxiv].]

How do you like tha. Tha's now real Limburg dialect.

In the north they have a different custom, they don't like no more bonfires here […] in old Dutch towns like Edam, Purmerend, Zaandam, Hoorn. But more an more in other towns the children go around in groups, with pack'o lanterns a different colours. These lanterns are sometimes made a hollow pumpkins with grinning an laughin faces. The children go around from door to door, and ringing the bell they sing they songs an ask for a few cents or some sweets or fruit.

In every part of the land they have their own songs, here is one tha they sing along in the Zaan:

[Intermission with music:
Hier woont een rijke man,

144

Die ons vast wat geven kan,
Geef een appel of een peer,
We komen 't hele jaar niet meer.
Sint Maarten, Sint Maarten,
de meisjes hebben staarten,
de koeien hebben rokjes aan,
*daar komt Sint Maarten aan*xxv. *]*

But not only big children go out serenading on Sint Maarten's but sometimes quite small ones go along with their bigger brother and sister, and sometimes even on the arm of their father. An especially these lil [ones] the people take fun in listening to, some a them can just stammer the words, an the moment you put something in they hands they stop singing and want to go the next door.

[Intermission with music]

Nice. lil thing oh.

But you mussen think that all the children who come beggin at the door on Sint Maarten are poor. No, every[one] goes on Sint Maarten, rich and poor, an they sing from door to door about the saint who helped the poor beggar hoping the people will follow his example and a lotta them do.

Here is the song they sing in Twente:

[Intermission with music
    Sinte, Sinte Marten,
    De kalvers dragen starten,
    De koeien dragen horens,
    De kerken dragen torens,
    Mooi meisjes dragen rokken,
    De jongens dragen broeken,
    Oude wijven schorteldoeken.

Sinten Maarten is zo koud,
Geef hem 'n turfje of een hout,
Daar kan hij 'm mee verwarmen,
Met zijn bloote armen,
Met zijn bloote bienen,
Dan kan hij een duitje verdienen[xxvi].

Till another time.
Goodnite folks.

Blessed rain, cursed rain

Broadcast January 19, 1952

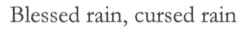

"Ho, Burro, ho! Brrr Jenny brrr. This gon be the last trip for this afternoon Jenny an then a turn you loose so you can look for food and a sho hope you can find sumpen to eat."

Merrill Nesbitt took the empty casks offa he donkey his back an after he had pulled out the plugs, he got up to the well an waited for he turn to draw water, while he chatted with men and boys tha he knew.

The only thing they could talk of was the drought: about how hot the weather was, how many cattle or sheep Tom, Dick or Harry had loose an then they started off telling stories about the rains they could remember.

All the cattle that the men was watering was meager and weak. An a lotta them looked like they would die even if the rain did come soon and the young grass would kill a lotta them. It had been dry for so long tha you coulden recognize the land around you if you had seen it when it was green, all the slobs in the country was dry an the people had to go far to get water for they stock. Merrill had to make six trips a day to Lower Quarter to get water from the well the government had build dung there.

This was the last trip of the day for he an he donkey Jenny. When he turn at the well had come Merrill full up he casks as quick as he could, an one of the men helped him put them on he donkey, one on either side.

"Now boys, till tomorrow", Merrill called out, *"look at tha....all the land look just like somebody been burning it off, not a green piece in sight..."*

When he passed the guard house he said hello to Jim the policeman who was stationed there. *"Man"*, he said to him, *"you don need to sit there all day t' ain no weather for people to go smuggling."*

"It just like you say Merrill", Jim answered *"but I prefer this job to*

being in town. Wha man it is so hot in town the people try to find all kinda excuses to keep off the streets an a bet you Melford's Cola plant got a lot to do these days if he can get water to make Cola with. Yeah, the people in tung must be drinking like fish to get a lil bit a coolness in this heat."

"No Jim just look at tha, the only green you see is the manzaneedles rung the Bay a Biscay an in the long bottom. [If] they an carshaws was good to eat, you shore woulden see such a lotta them in this weather. Now Jim, a gon roll along, till another time. So long."

And Merrill shuffled past One Hoe up Bishop Hill, past the well yard, up hill past the big bull-head mango tree and turn in to Middle Region where he use to live. He empty he casks in the coppers an after he had turn Jenny loose he went in the house for a cool drink outta a guglet. Then he went up Naked Boy for he cow, he put it in he lil pen back a the house. Back a he house he had, or use to have a lil grung, but now everything was dry up. Goin inside Merrill washed heself up a bit an sat dung till he wife called him in for he meal a salt fish an rice.

After they had finish eating, Anna, Merrill wife wash up the things and Merrill sat dung outside on the step talking to the neighbor who was an Anguillaman. When it was dark Anna light the lamp an came out to talk with the men when she had finish her work.

"Ah sho hope we get some rain tonite", Merrill said, an lookin up at the sky he noticed the few clouds tha was sailing along. *"It's a good thing we don't have any fires here otherwise the woulden even have water to stop the whole place from burning down."*

The Anguillaman had been to town an so he could tell them all the latest news. After chatting for a few hours the Nesbitts said good night and turned in. In a short time the lite was turned down an everything about the house was quiet. Now an then you hear a dog barking in the distance an further on another one would answer, the noise going further an further till it died away all together.

In the middle of the nite Merrill woke.....he sat up in bed listening an turned an shook he wife.

"Anna, woman, wake up, it rainin."

"Yes Merril a know it been rainin for the last half hour."

"Why didden you wake me, you wimmin get me sick sometimes, you don't excited atall."

When Merrill got up the next morning he had to put a kruger hat over he head before going outside: it was still raining an after Merrill had done he regular morning work he took out he hoe up he groung. It rained all day that day, with very heavy showers in between drizzles and it kept up for two days more. By tha time Merrill had he grung ready for planting an the moment the rain stopped he started to put in he seeds.

The same afternoon it had stopped raining Joe Samuel passed along (while Merrill was working in he grung) an stopped to make small talk: *"Man you should see the sight all rung the country. All the slobs full, the dam dung Belvedère still running over un you should see the signt on you way to town, all the roads washed out, the salt ponds full a water and the dam burst just pass the thatch houses. Man they had to work like the dickens to keep the water from coming in the town. Everybody work like they did before trying to stop the water with bags a mud. They sure was glad when it stopped rainin."*

"Yea", Merrill answered, *"but a betcha everybody was glad when it started to rain. One thing is sure, a lotta people gon loose stock when the young grass start coming, but if it hadden rain, a lot more woudda died. Now Joe a got to get on with me work. Be seeing you."*

Merrill walked back over to he grung an went on where he had left off an Joe went on where he had left off an Joe went on up Middle Region.

Goodnite folks.

Damn goats!

Broadcast April 19, 1952

"Now look here Jim Nisbett, a tellin you for the last time…. Keep you goats outta ma grung. If a catch them on me land again a gon sue you for damages or a gon set me dog on them. A been warning enough. You old goats always running dung me wall an eating off all the young shoots off me plants. Up to now a only been working for those goats a yours. A ain't gon stand it no longer 't is enough to make a saint lose he patience."

"Ayo looka work, a tole you John Simon, a doing ma bes to keep those goats off you place. But the moment a turn me back they over the wall. But tain only my goats that eating up you pidginpeas trees, they a lotta goats running aroung that belong to Tommy Jones an others…."

"Alright Jim Nisbett a don't care who they belong to but if a catch them in me grung again they gon be the devil to pay. An don't say a diddin warn you, good day to you."

An John Simon turn arung an walkin through the gate he went home to eat. After he had finish he food he went up Lower Quarter and sat dung with a lotta others and chatted about all the news tha some had bring from Great Bay or from Marigot.

They had been a big haul a jacks in Marigot and the Hodges in Grand Case were building a new schooner. Capen Johannes had just come from Macoris and was leave us a few days with a load a salt from Orion Bay for Guadeloup. In the Agricultural garden they had a new bull, a Frisian Holstein tha had just been shipped out from Holland to replace the one tha had died a couple a months before. So the men sat dung smoking they pipe or sigar an exchanging news.

Sam de Weever had get a chook from a cushaw, an because he whole arm had been infected the doctor was afraid he'd lose he arm. But Sam said: *"If a got to lose it let rab off, no saw bones gon get a chance to cut me up."*

Around ten o'clock one after the other a the men got up, said

155

good night an went home. So John Simon got up an walked down the road to he lil house. He turned in at once, because he wife had gone to bed already. The next morning bright and early both a them was up and about getting things ready to go weed in they grung before the sun was up.

Round ten o'clock they stopped working and sat dung in the shade of a tammond tree to drink the coffee. After that Gatey, John's wife, went home to cook. They grung wassent far from home and so John use to go home every afternoon to eat. At twelve o'clock Simon stopped the weedin and went to the house for grub a lil wash up. After they finish the salt fish and rice, John took he dog Nero and went up to the grung.

The moment he turn the Bay a Biskay he saw they was four goats in he grung eating away in he young pidgin peas trees. So John started running. *"A gon get those good for nothing things this time. Come on Nero, go get them."* An he set he dog loose callin out: *"Get them Nero"*.

Without a sound Nero started after the goats an one after the other he catch hold of a hind leg or a throat an held fast till John came up with a piece a rope to tie the animal fast. So Simon and Nero catch three a the four goats. Only one got away but not without getting a few good bites from Nero's sharp teeth.

"Good boy, Nero", John said to he dog, *"now less take these animals down to the guardhouse to put them in pound."* He looked around he grung before leavin to see what damages had been done an fixed up the fence where the goats had bust through.

Jim Hassell had duty at the guardhouse an when Simon showed up with the goats he was sittin dung under the tommand tree reading a book.

"Ah see yo got some pen there for me John. Who they belong to?"

"Yes Jim, a catch these pests in me grung an a don care who they belong to, a got to get back the damages they done to me grung."

Jim tied the goats fast and John went home to tell he wife the news. In the evening the owners a the goats, Sam Nesbitt an John de Weever came to John's house an they bargained out the damages they had to pay.

"Anyhow", John Simon said, *"a don't want to catch anymore a these beasts in me land. Next time a gon let Nero kill them. But a don hope they gon be a next time."*

"No John, we both promise yo they ain gon be a next time."

Smugglin trick

Broadcast July 12, 1952

Long time gone by they use to be a lotta smuggling goin on between the States and the French islands in the West Indies. In those days the whole a America was living under prohibition an bootleggers was makin lotta money sellin smuggled whiskey, gin and rum.

Lotta this drinks came from Saint Martin, Nearly every week three or four small ships with powerful engines would be loading in Marigot with cases an cases of spirits. These ships use to run to some lil harbor along the American coast or they was loaded in small motorboats.

Also up to not long ago they was a kinda prohibition on the Dutch side a Sint Maarten too: taxes on alcohol was high although you could get all kinds a drinks on the French side for nothing.

In these days they use to be a lotta smuggling and the police in guardhouses had a lotta work trying to catch people who was trying to bring somethings across without paying taxes. Anybody that was caught lost he rum an got a fine, and the rum was taken to town and sold or it was thrown off the wharf in the sea.

Over in Cole Bay Charley Thomas was in the guardhouse, an from early in the morning till late in the night, an sometimes all night, he'd be out searching an now an then he'd butt up against somebody with a demijohn or with a couple bottles. But most a the smugglers got away because after they had been caught once, they learned the trick a bringin across the liquor in one place while the police was lookin in another place.

Jim Peters and Tom Yates was always smuggling, an they'd sell the liquor in Great Bay for a good price.

"We ain't never gon get caught once we careful: Jim, this time it you turn to bring across the liquor. I gon watch out for Charley, and if he come too near you a gon make a good noise so you and he can hear an a gon start running to get him come after me, so you can get away." In tha way Jim got away an brought the rum to town safely.

161

Tha same week Charley caught a fellow from Cul de Sac who come walking dung the road with a kerosene pan on the head, like he was carrying water in it. Charley was sitting dung on a wall lookin up the road when this fellow come along. An it is only tha luck on he side that Charley found out there was rum in the pan: just as the fellow was passin Charley he stubbed he toe an stumbled: a lotta rum splashed over the a the can. Charley smellin the liquor jumped off the wall and grabbed the fellow.

Jim and Jo use to cross over in a different place every time. An if policeman was anywhere arung they'd have a new trick to get across. Sometimes they go to Marigot for the liquor and then they'd go to French Quarter buy they spirits there an come across somewhere between Belplain and Oysterpoint.

In the guardhouse by Anette was a policeman who was [a] very careful fellow an he was onea those fellows who you coulden fool easily. Jo and Jim had been trying for instance to work out a new plan to bring cross a good boad a rum from French Quarter. Both a them would come cross the Bay a Biskay each with a donkey with two big casks a rain water they'd fetch from Belplain: an they had made up they mind to keep coming across till the policeman, whose name was Sam Arindell, stopped lookin into they casks an then they'd put rum in them.

But as a tole yo Sam was a very careful policeman an every day that Jim and Jo came along he'd meet them somewhere along the road:

"Who a what ayo got in those casks."

"Water."

"You sure a tha?"

"Quite sure..."

And Sam would take a stick an feel around inside all the casks an after tha he'd smell the stick. Every day was the same thing an after a week Jim an Jo had to give up they plan. But they was so vexed with Sam that they thought they play a good trick on him to stop him being so careful. They thought and they planned an at last Jim got a good idea an they decided to try it right away.

The very next morning Sam was sittin under the tammon tree on the wall by the guardhouse when he see Jim an Jo turn the corner, both a them rollin a big cask in front a him. When they come up to him he stopped them calling out: "*Wha you got there....*"

"*Two casks a cowdung*", Jim answered. But Sam who was a careful man pulled the plug outta the barrels an he smelled them: "*Tha cow musta been weaned in a rumshop*", he said. "*This is rum. Where the devil you think you was goin with this casks.*"

"*Oh, we was only goin to town with them.*"

"*Oh you. They were goin to town an you gon get a good fine for smuggling, both a yo, an yo rum gon be sold or thrown in the sea.*"

So Sam had the two barrels taken to town. But Jim an Jo had warned a lotta people to come an see the joke. So everybody gathered on the wharf an the receiver was there to see tha everything went right. First they tried to sell the rum, but nobody wanted to buy it, because they could get it much cheaper in Marigot. So the Brigadier told Sam to knock the top outta the casks an let the liquor run into the sea.

Sam took up a pickaxe an...... guess wha happened..... the moment he broke the top in he said: "*Wha the dickens, ...ayo looka trouble....*" And a lotta other words a can repeat here an which he wouda never said in fronta the Brigadier an all the folks standing arung if he hadden been so surprised. He turned aroun an knocked the top outta the other cask an he looked even still more surprised (if tha was possible).

All the people stretched they necks an pushed to get a good look; then they all burst out laughin so hard yo could hear it on the Backstreet..... They was rum in the barrels, but just a lil bit round the plug for the smell, for the rest the whole thing was packed fulla cowdung.

Goodnight folks.

Mongoose sorrow

Broadcast August 11, 1952

The sun had just come up in the east, an as yet the day was cool an the dew shining on the grass an leaves a the trees. Now an then yo could hear a thrush callin in a soursap tree, a couple a chincerries was chasin a quackin gaolin, mountain-doves and ground-doves was cooeing, an in the distance a cow was callin her calf; the milkin was done an the men driven the cattle out to the pasture for the day.

Papa Mongoose stretched heself, while he opened first one eye then the other.

"*Common folks, it time to wake up*", he called to he wife an children. "*Open ye eyes lil rascals, last night ye didden want to sleep an now ye lazy like the dickens*", and he grabbed two a he children by they tails and pulled them outta they beds. In a moment the house was bustling with noise while the four lil mongoose ran rung chasin one another.

Meantime Popa and Moma had gone outside to look about an see if everything was allright.

"*It gon be a fine day, for the children to start goin out in the world, but Popa ye must not forget to tellem about all the dangers they gon meet. A so frighten – a feel like they too young yet to leave us – especially lil Jim – he gon walk in the first trap he butt up on...*"

"*Ah woman, don humbug up a man. Ayo wimmin always fussin about everything an yo doin just like yo can smell troubles miles off. Yo gon see tha the children can take care a themselves. Just listen to the noise they makin in there, yo can hear that they excited to know wha happenin outside a bungrung... But a just as anxious as you about them, come less get it finished.*"

The children was called outside, an Popa mongoose clearin he throat started: "*Now children, today is a big day for yo, but before yo leave us yo mother an I have some advice to give yo. Remember all a tole you about dogs, traps an men with guns, don get outta a wall without lookin rung to see if the coast is clear, an keep off the big roads, because they dangerous. If yo meet any a yo kind be polite to them, a don want people sayin a didden learn ayo manner. Remember all a tole ye an ye have chance a getting old. People learn by makin mistakes a hear, but mongoose can afford to make mistakes. Alright now, solong an good luck…"*

The mongoose kissed they mother and shooh the fathers hand, then they set off two by two.

Charley and lil Jim went to Jonsgut an on they way there they has all kinds a adventures. They'd catch a grungdove or a small mountaindove tha had fallen outta he nest, an it was funny but everytime they'd be hungry they'd find sumpen to eat.

One morning when they was nearin Jonsgut they was awakend by a big explosion near the wall in which they was sleepin, an peepin out they saw a man with a double barreled gun walkin arung as if he was lookin for something.

"A betcha he just shot a mountain-dove an he can find it", Jimmy said.

"A ain gon bet because ye would win, a can see the dove walkin between the fizzicnuts over there, she got a broken wing. The moment the fellow turn he back a goin out to get her, she sho look fat an sweet."

"Ye mussen do thd", Jim argued, *"ye know wha Popa told us about men with guns, he gon shoot ye fer sure."*

"Ah, stop yo talkin before ye wakeup the whole neighbourhood. T'ain more than ten yards an a can get out there before yo can say ballahoo…"

So Charley waited till the man had he back turned, then he jumped outta the wall an rushed to where he had seen the dove last. When the bird saw him comin it started to flutter around an make a lotta noise in the bush. The man hear this commotion, but he coulden see because the bush was too thick. Charley got the dove in he mouth an started running for the wall, but the moment he reached the open space between the bush and the place where he brother was hidin, the hunter fired, givin the mongoose the full load. With the bird still in he mouth Charley kicked out he last life on the grung.

Jim was so frightened when he saw he brother drop dead with the explosion a the shot tha he started runnin an didden stop till he reached Jonsgut where he stopped at his uncle Tom's house. An he was the only one a he brothers to get away from the dangers a the big world they had gone out to explore.

Dick was caught out in the open one day by a dog while he was goin to a slob to drink, and although he run like greased lightening the dog outrun him. Harry got trapped while he was sleepin in a wall tha a goat run dung. A big rock struck him on the head an he never know what t' wus hit him.

But Jimmy married he niece Susy an lived for years an years in Jonsgut. An got old before the dangers a the world caught up with him. But tha a story a gon tell yo another time.

Black rocks and magic fish

Droudourst TsTuuuuuubur 18, 1952

Hello folks, tonite yo gon hear one a ma last stories. A been tellin ayo these tales now for about four year an a sho hope ye all liked them as much as a liked tellin them.

All ayo know where th Black Rocks be at the head a tung, but a bet none a yo know how come the rocks are black an they come there?...No....? Lemme tell you....

Once upon a time, it was a long time ago, before Great Bay was Great Bay, and in the days when the salt-ponds was still sea an there was no need for a bank to protect them, in those days they use to live a fellow at the foot a Naked Boy Hill (in those day tha wassen the name a the hill). This fellow's name was Joseph Mathias White: Joseph after the father, an Mathias because he mother had like the name.

White an he brother Granville use ta live in they lil cowdung-kingdom with a thatch-roof. Joseph Mathias was a fellow no bigger than the ordinary man, but he had mouth that was much bigger. He use ta brag about everything he had done or even about somethings he had not done: for he was a big liar to boot. He was very jealous a he brother, because Granville was taller an broader than he and because he didden lie. Granville was respected by everyone, and he could get as much work to do as he wanted, but Joseph was lazy.

Together they use to work they lil grung in the hill an haul fishpots in the bay.

One day Joseph had one a he lazy spells. He went to sleep under a tammond tree back at the house, so Granville had to go out an haul up an empty they fishpots alone.

Granville pushed they boat out from under the manzaneedle tree dung by the bayside where they use to keep it, he jumped in and rowed out to the first pot just left a the bar - the ole bar a mean on which in later years Great Bay was built.

When he got near the marker float he steadied the boat an hauled hauled in the pot. The only thing inside was a lil yellow-tail and a big fat conga tha, it was plain to see, had eaten heself full up to the point a burstin on the fish tha had been in the pot.

"Yo sure is genereous Mister conga", Granville said. *"You coulda eaten everything but you leave me this one yellow-tail, a gon fix you so you can eat no more outta our pots."*

An he smashed the head [of] conga with a piece a wood an threw him overboard for the other fish to eat. While he was doing tha the lil yellow tail lay quite still in the bottom a the boat lookin at Granville.

"Mister Granville", the fish said after a while, *"you is a good man, a know tha an a kin see it in yo face. Throw me back in the sea an a gon make you rich an happy; anything you want from me you can get."*

"Ayo looka trouble, a talkin fish, a catch a talkin fish", Granville called out. *"A don want a lot lil yellow tail, a just want to stop our house from leakin, a ain got time to fix it meself an me brother can fix thatch roofs."*

"Yo wish is the wish of a man who issen greedy, Mister Granville. Everytime you come haul yo pot on this side a the bank, you gon find [me] an a gon be ready to fulfill you wishes."

Granville thanked the yellow tail an laid him back in the water. So it came to pass tha they thatched roof stopped leaking, the goats stopped busting into they grung, they cow had a cow-calf and they fishin-boat got a new bottom.

But one morning Granville coulden go out to he fishpots an he coulden work at all, he had to stay in bed with the grippe. Granville started thinkin about all the work he had to do an all of which nothing would be done because he brother was so lazy. At last he called Joseph and told him about the lil yellow tail askin him to go to the fishpot on the lefthand side of the bar an ask the lil fish to make him better so he could do he work.

"Yo mean to tell me yo been keepin this magic fish all for yoself, without askin him for a big house with lots a servants an lots a money so tha we would never have to work again? You good for nothing... Yo greedy like the dickens otherwise you woulda ask the fish for something for me too.""

Granville didden feel like arguing so he turn he face to the wall after asking Joseph Mathias once more to go out to the fish pots for him. But Joseph keep on summin up all the greavances he had against he brother while he got angrier an angrier all the time. By the time all he blood vessels was fit to burstin he picked up a chair, an smashing it on he brothers head killed him.

He went outside an digging a big hole in the grung back a the house, he berried Granville in it. After tha he took the boat an rowing out to the bar pulled up the fishpot in which Granville had told him he'd find the magic fish.

"Lil yellow tail", Joseph said when the pot was in the boat, *"me brother send me to ask yo somethings for him."*

"How come yo brother didden come heself?"

"He coulden come because he was too busy and he wanted yo to give us a big house an lots a servants an money so we woulden have to work any more an...."

"Joseph White yous' a liar... yo killed yo own brother an yo greedy black soual tells you to ask for all this. Yo can fool me...."

"Lo[rd] lil yellow tail...., a telling the truth, a always tell the truth...."

But the yellow tail told him to shut up and stop lying.

"*A liked Granville, because he was a good man an because you killed him a gon have you punished. You name is White but you soul is black, you so bad ye black throu and throu. For your punishment a gon turn you in rocks as black as you soul and you boat gon sink with yo right here….*"

At the same time the lil yellow tail was outta the fishpot an in the water.

Joseph was so frightened he coulden move and as the yellow tail had said he turned to black rock and he boat sunk right where we has near the left had side a the ole bar.

Tha is the story about the black rocks an whenever you pass them or sit on them to rest, remember Joseph an what jealousy an greed can do to a man.

Good night folks!

Ole year

Broadcast December 31, 1952

Hello folks,

At the end of every year we look back on the months, weeks and days tha have past an the 31st of December is always a day of sadness an rejoicing.

Of sadness because on this day we think of all those of our family an friends who are not here to spend this day with us, we think of all the mishaps that overcome us all, sickness, death an all other kinda troubles.

But on this day we are glad and rejoice for the new year which we see before us an we wish everybody a happy new year an everything else that can be wished.

Just like when a babe is born in this world the whole family rejoice, so we all are happy an make merry at the coming of this new year we see dawning before us, hopin it will bring the sick good health, the weak strength and everybody prosperity.

We share this evening with our family and good friends, at the chimes of the clock striking twelve everybody raise their glasses an drink to everybody elses" health, while outside sirens are howlin an horns are blowin, bells are ringin, fire-crackers are crackin an rockets bursting in the sky, to demonstrate the goodwill all of us start the new year with, an to show our happiness with the birth of 1953.

Though I hope to be with part of my family and friends, I gratefully take this chance to wish all family an friends wherever they be a very happy new year an a sure that as I am going to do, all the students from the Antills here in Holland and far from all they folks, are goin to raise they glasses tonight an thinkin of you all, drink to your very good health.

So on behalf of the windward islanders in the Netherlands an myself, I wish you all a very happy an prosperous New Year, a joyfull 1953. Goodnight.

Glossary
Reading assistance for
'Ole tales, sweet memories'

Word as written to approach as much as possible the phonetically colloquial use | Meaning can be different from case to case and must be derived from the context, where relevant.

A

'a' — 'a', 'an', 'I', or 'of'
'abeen' — 'have been'
'agin' — 'again'
'ain' 'ain't' or 'aint' — 'am not', 'have not' or 'is not', 'are not'
'aks' — 'ask'
'aksin', 'askin' — 'asking'
'a'll' — 'I will'
'altho' — 'although'
'an' — 'and'
'arung', 'aroun' — 'around'
'atall' — 'at all'
'ayo' — 'you' plural, probably a contraction of 'all of you'

'ayo looka trouble' or 'ayo looka work' — Expression of surprise and irritation, probably a contraction of 'All of you, look what a trouble'

B

'bad' — 'bad' or 'bath'
'bade' — 'bath' (past tense)
'bar' — 'sandbar' or 'sandbank'
'befor' — 'before'
'berried' — 'buried'
'bes' — 'best'
'betcha' — 'bet you'
'blaireye' — a fish with eyes like blears
'bungrung' — 'burned ground'
'burstin', 'bustin' — 'bursting'

182

C

'can'	'can' or 'cannot'
'cane'	'sugar cane', which was grown on the island long and made into sugar, molasses and rum. Commercial cane production stopped in the early twenthieth century
'capin', 'capen'	'captain'
'carshaw'	pronounced as 'kusha' or 'cosha' a very thorny bush with hard and long thorn needles. Needs very little water to thrive. Gives little fluffy yellow flowers when in bloom.
'chincerries'	bird, (tyrannus dominicensis)
'chook'	'prick'
'cole pots'	'coal pots', made of clay or cast iron, used for cooking, usually outside, with charcoal as fuel.
'come'	'come' or 'become'
'conger', 'conga'	a marine conger eel or moray eel with a snakelike body (gymnothorax moringa)
'conqshells'	'conch shells', (lobatus gigas)
'copper'	Very large cast iron bowl, originally used in the sugar and rum production to burn molasses
'cornin'	'corning', a method of food preservation in the time when there were no refrigerators, through salt-curing (brining, pickling, kippering).
'cornmeal'	a cheap and simple staple food, often eaten with fish in the Caribbean either as a stiff mass,

	a porridge, or fried.
'couden', 'coulden'	'could not'
'covalley'	fish, not certain which species, probably a crevalle jack (caranx hippos)
'cussin'	'cursing'

D

'debbels'	'devils'
'dey'	'they' or 'their'
'demijohn'	'Demijohn' is an old word that formerly referred to any glass vessel with a large body (5 to 15 gallons) and small neck, sometimes enclosed in wickerwork.
'didden', 'diddin', 'didn', 'did'n'	'did not'
'do'	'door'
'doctors'	Doctor fish, blueish greenish grey fish (acanthurus chirurgus)
'doin'	'doing'
'don'	'do not' or 'don't'
'dotin'	'doting', simple-minded, foolish
'drung'	'drowned'
'dung' or 'dong'	'dung' as in cow dung, or 'down'
'durin'	'during'

E

'en'	'end'

F

'feller'	'fellow'
'fer'	'for'
'fiels'	'fields'
'fine'	'fine' or "find'
'fishpot'	a trap to catch fish made of wicker or chicken mesh. This method of taking the fish or shellfish alive is widely practiced by local fishermen to supply fresh fish.
'fo'	'for', 'four'
'fraid'	'afraid'
'frighten'	'frightened'
'(in) fronta'	'in front of'
'fust'	'first'
'fulla'	'full of'

G

'gaolin'	bird, green heron (butorides virescens)
'gon', 'goin'	'am gone', 'are gone' 'is gone', or 'am going (to)', 'is going (to)', 'are going (to)' reflecting the future tense, or 'went'.
'got'	'have', 'has'
'grape-trees'	shade giving tree (coccoloba uvifera) with large round leaves found near the beaches and growing plentiful at Le Gallion Beach. Fruit baring. Its fruit look like grapes.
'grung'	'ground'
'grungdove'	'ground dove' (columbina passerina)
'grunt'	small silver colored fish with bright yellow stripes, (haemulon

chrysagyreum)

'guglet'	A long-necked earthenware vessel for holding water and keeping it cool in a hot climate.

H

'hadden'	'had not'
'he'	'he' or 'his'
'heddanever'	'he would never have'
'heed' or 'he'd'	'he would'
'heself'	'himself'
'hookja'	'hook you'

I

'I'd'	'I would'
'if't'	'If it'
'issen'	'is not'

J

'jack o'lantern'	a lantern carved from a pumpkin
'jacks'	fish, (caranx latus), or (caranx ruber), commonly swims with others in a school, either as one species or mixed with jack species.
'jus'	'just'

K

'kep'	'kept'
'kin'	'can'
'kinda'	'kind of'
'kingfish'	fish, (scomberomorus cavalla), or 'wahoo' (acanthocybium solandri)
'kno'	'know'

L

'Lamejo'
Colloquial contraction of the French name 'Baie de l'Embouchure', locally also known as Coconut Grove or Le Gallion Beach. Located on the north east of the island on the French side.

'law-abidin' — 'law abiding'
'lef' — 'left'
'lemme' — 'let me'
'less' — 'less' or 'let us'
'lickerd' — 'liquored'
'like the dickens'
Meaning
'a lot' or 'very'; as in 'hurts like the dickens'.
Origin
This phrase has nothing to do with Charles Dickens. Dickens is a euphemism, specifically a minced-oath, for the word devil, possibly via devilkins. Shakespeare used it in 'the Merry Wives of Windsor, 1600:
"I cannot tell what the dickens his name is my husband had him of". [xxvii]
Uncertain if this expression is used colloquially on Sint Maarten or is the result of the classical study at Rolduc Gymnasium.

'lil' — 'Little'
'lite' — 'light'
'lotta' — 'a lot of'
'lun' — 'learn', 'reach'

M

'machete'
: a large cleaver like knife, used (amongst others) to cut sugar cane

'Macorice'
: Probably San Pedro de Macorís, a municipality with a harbour on Santo Domingo

'maken'
: 'making'

'manzaneedle tree'
: 'manchineel tree' (hippomane mancinella). The name 'manchineel' (sometimes written 'manchioneel') as well as the specific epithet mancinella is from Spanish manzanilla ('little apple'), from the superficial resemblance of its fruit and leaves to those of an apple tree.

A present-day Spanish name is in fact manzanilla de la muerte, 'little apple of death'. This refers to the fact that manchineel is one of the most poisonous trees in the world.

'me'
: 'me', 'my' or 'mine'

'meself'
: 'myself'

'mo'
: 'more'

'mongoose'
: 'mongoose' (herpestes javanicus auropunctatus), a small terrestrial carnivorous ferret-like mammal belonging to the family Herpestidae.

Originally of Asian origin, the mongoose brought to the islands in the late 19th and early 20th centuries to control

rats in sugar cane fields, but also

	to control snakes.
'mus'	'must'
'mussen', 'mun't'	'must not'
'musta'	'must have'

N

'nex'	'next'
'nite'	'night'
'nitegungs'	'nightgown'
'no more'	'not anymore'
'nut'	'not
'nuthun'	'nothing'

O

'o'	'of'
'oi'	'I'
'ole'	'old'
'ole wife'	fish (trachinotus goodei)
'outta'	'out of'

P

'pack o'lantern'	(self made) paper lanterns replacing the jack o'lantern.
'pelikins'	'pelicans' large sea birds that make up the family Pelecanidae. They are characterized by a long beak and a large throat pouch used for catching fish (pelecanus occidentalis occidentalis)
'pickin'	'picking'
'pidginpeas'	'pigeon peas', (cajanus cajan), pigeon peas are very drought resistant and stewed part of the local cuisine,

	eaten with rice.
'pilot fish'	fish (naucrates ductor), swims along with sharks.
'pliesman'	'policeman'
'po'	'poor'
'pots'	'fishpots', 'coal pots' or 'cooking pots'.

R

'railin'	'railing'
'rainin'	'raining'
'red snapper'	very tasty red fish (Lutjanus campechanus)
'reminin'	'reminding'
'rocker'	'rocking chair'
'round', 'rung', 'arung'	'around'

S

'sain'	'saying'
'salt heap'	Once collected ('picked') salt was stored in huge heaps on the side of the salt pond pending transportation.
'salt pickin'	The collection of salt once crystalized in the salt ponds. Very hard work under very difficult circumstances. Sint Maarten/Saint Martin hailed various salt ponds and salt was exported until the mode of collection and market circumstances no longer made it a viable economic activity.
'sea island cotton'	a variety of cotton (gossypi-

um barbadense), which long ago was grown on the Sint Maarten and exported in small scale.

'sensiblest'	'most sensible'
'she'	'she' or 'her'
'sho'	'sure'
'shobbed'	'shoved'
'shouden-a'	'should not have'
'side'	'side' or 'aside (of)'
'slob'	'slough', a natural collection point of rainwater, which may be sporadically filled, depending on the season.
'soursap'	'soursop', (annona muricata), is a green skinned fruit with small dull spikes containing white slimy flesh and black seeds. The flavour has been described as a combination of strawberry and pineapple, with sour citrus flavour notes contrasting with an underlying creamy flavour reminiscent of coconut or banana. Spanish name: guanabanana.
'such'	'such' or 'search'
'sumpen', 'sompthing'	

T

'ta'	'to'
'tammond tree'	'tamarind tree' (tamarindus indica). The tamarind is a long-lived, medium-growth,

	bushy tree which grows well in full sun with a high drought and aerosol salt resistance. The tamarind tree produces edible, pod-like fruit which are used extensively in cuisines around the world.
't'ain'	'it will not (be)'
't'ain gon bi no need'	'it will not be necessary'
'tellem'	'tell them'
'tha', 'tha's'	'that', 'that is'
'they'	'they', 'their' or 'there'
'they'd'	'they would'
'they'nt'	'there are no(t)'
'they's been'	'there have been'
'theyselves'	'themselves'
'tho'	'although'
'throu'	'through'
'thrush'	bird, known as 'thrush' or Pearly-eyed Thrasher (margarops fuscatus)[xxviii]
'till'	'until'
'tis'	'It is'
'tole'	'told'
'tonite'	'tonight'
'tung'	'town'
't'wus'	'it was'

U

'ud'	'would'
'umpty'	'empty'
'use'	'use', 'used'

V

'Ver''	'Very'

W

'wa' or 'wha'	'what'
'watlin'	'wattling' a sort of woven work made of sticks intertwined with twigs or branches
'walkin'	'walking'
'wan'	'want'
'wassen', 'wassent', 'was'n'	'was not', 'were not'
'wasn't'	'was not', 'were not'
'we'en'	'we are not'
'whe'	'where'
'wimmin'	'women'
'winders'	'windows'
'wi nt'	'will not'
'worl'	'would'
'woud', 'wud'	'would'
'woulda'	'would have'
'womin'	'women'
'wooden'	'would not'

Y

'ye', 'you' or 'yo'	'you' or 'your'
'yellowtail'	fish with a yellow tail, ocyurus chysurus
'you'd'	'you would'
'yous''	'you are'

Acknowledgement

There are so many friends, family members and others, who I really must acknowledge for encouraging me to finally publish 'Ole tales, sweet memories', that I hope I won't forget anyone. Please forgive if my memory has failed me and I forgot to mention your name.

Everybody seems keen to read the stories. Some can simply not wait to read about the humble man who wrote them, a man they respected and loved and who unfortunately died far too young at the age of 62.

It is fitting however that I single out some people in particular:

Dr. Jos de Roo, who found the 18 stories whilst doing research for his thesis. I am thankful that he was prepared to add an introductory chapter about his extraordinary find. Without him this book would not have been possible.

My mother Ellie Plantz and my siblings Yvette Plantz, Rufus Plantz and Astrid Plantz who sanctioned this endeavour.

The many friends and family members who shared family anecdotes and pictures from their private collections: Yvette Fleming Hodge, Danny Hodge, Maurice Gumbs, Louis Richardson, Vere Richardson, Cynthie Richardson, Louis Duzanson, Frank Richards, Ellie Plantz, Gon Tromp, Ruben Beauperthuy, Joyce Wathey, Irma Mulder, Frans Mulder, Olette Hyman, Will Johnson, Marcel Gumbs, Annie Brooke Fleming, Edward Brooke, Louis Constant Fleming, Ferdie Beauperthuy, Karine Fleming... Some have passed away since sharing the anecdotes and unfortunately will never read the final product.

People who have given me access to valuable sources used for this book: Louis 'Math' Dicker of 'Stichting Leve Rolduc' for providing me digital copies of the yearbooks of the years my father attended 'Rolduc', Mark Yokoyama for providing me with invaluable access to his book 'An incomplete guide to the wildlife of Saint Martin', Bill Burns of FTL Design, owner of the on-line history 'Atlantic Cable - the History of Undersea Communications: 1850-2019' , who even sent me the engineering plans of cable ship 'Grappler'.

And very important: two dear friends for life, who were the first readers of the manuscript and helped with correcting the English and editing the text. Their efforts have certainly enriched the story line flow for the reader and made the end product much better than it was when they got the rough manuscript: Mary Snow Helmund, owner of the 'Daily Herald' newspaper of Sint Maarten and Lynn Kaplanian Buller, owner of the 'American Book Center' in Amsterdam and The Hague.

And last but not least, by husband Henk, son Len and daughter Roxanne who have lovingly supported me in all the crazy adventures I have undertaken, so far

I am thankful that this adventure has come to fruition.

Maria

Notes

i "In de Nederlandse Antillen worden de Nanzi-verhalen, behalve op de Papiamentstalige eilanden, ook nog aangetroffen op Sint Eustatius."

ii Recorded in a notarial deed dated January 5, 1938 and January 20, 1938

iii Recorded in a notarial deed dated January 3, 1938

iv http://www.wazamar.org/Bonaire/genealogieen/gezin-plantz-de-geneste.htm

v http://www.rootsweb.ancestry.com/~vicgl/Caron/MontPeleeEruption.pdf

vi http://atlantic-cable.com//Cableships/Grappler/index.htm

vii **The Loss of the S.S. Grappler**
Oh Grappler boys who left our land
Truly they were a loving band;
Duty sent them to foreign sands
To fall by death's relentless hands.

When last this crew in joy had met
Can either you or I forget?
'T was at the wedding of a friend
Who never dream'd of such an end.

On Monday's eve the fifth of May,
When forth she went on duty's way,

Many and bitter were the tears
From those who cherished doubts and fears.

Yet when she went behind the hills,
 None did expect so many ills,
When all of us did lose the view
Who thought 't was our last adieu?

But so it was, and so 't will be
Until the deep and greedy sea
 Shall yield from out her bosom deep
Lov'd ones, who now in her do sleep.

For cable ends they went to seek
Close to the shores of Martinique;
Where fate, alas, had seal'd their lot,
And doom'd just there, their resting spot.

From Mount Pelée's tremendous height
Came flames and rocks with speed and might,
Destroying lives and mansions dear
Which just before were bright and fair.

How awful must have been the sound
Which came from that destructive mound,
While helpless souls sent mercy cries
To Him who dwells above the skies.

 Let neither wives nor mothers weep
For them that rest within the deep
The time will come when every heart
Will meet, no more, no more to part.

The Grappler and her gallant crew
Are all forever lost from view,
BOREHAM's command will never more
Guide ship nor friends to our shore.

viii Hoofdmoment uit de Staatkundige Ontwikkeling van de Nederlandse

Antillen 1865 -1986, Dr. A.F. de Paula,
http://books.caribseek.com/Curacao/Staatkundige Ontwikkeling Nederlandse Antillen

[ix] According to the records of Mr. Albert Buncapmer transcribed in Will
Johnson's Diary of a St. Martin Salt Checker (page 84) for the year 1927:
"June 12th. . Schooner "George Town" arrived today between two and here
o'clock . Passengers Plantz'wife, child and Plantz mother."

[x] Visa granted January 26, 1934

[xi] Government Decree dated January 1934

[xii] Will Johnson, 'For the love of Sint Maarten',
http://books.caribseek.com/Sint_Maarten/For_The_Love_Of_St_Maarten/

[xiii]From https://thesabaislander.com/2014/page/5/author Will Johnson :
"it is remarkable how similar the news was back then to now. Brouwer was
involved in politics. In those days two local councilors were elected by the
moneyed class to advise the Lt. Governor on local matters. Brouwer ran
amuck with the elections and brought out the coters who in the past had
shown lukewarm interest in voting. As few as four people would take part
in the leection before Brouwers time. He also ran for the position of representative in the parliament. Rufus Plantz was the favoured candidate of the
Amigoe the newspaper on Curacao owned by the Catholic Church. Brouwer dug up Plantz birth certificate, proving that Plantz' mother was a de
Geneste from St. Eustatius and his father was aGerman, and Plantz had
been born on St. Thomas and baptized a Protestant. Nevertheless Plantz
won that election in 1936. Brouwer had a field day in throwing out for
public review gossip about Plantz and the fact that technically he was a
foreigner."

[xiv] He is clearly visible on the class photo in Rolduc's Jaarboek XXIV,
1944, page 152.

[xv] Rolduc's Jaarboek XXIV, 1944, page 110, June 14th, 1944

[xvi] Rolduc's Jaarboek XXIV, 1944, page 97

[xvii] Rolduc's Jaarboek XXIII, 1943, page 26, May 27th, 1943

xviii Rolduc's Jaarboek XXIV, 1944, page 110, June 14th, 1944

xix Grammar is the study of rules governing the use of language. The set of rules governing a particular language is the grammar of that language. Traditional grammars include only morphology and syntax. Syntax is the study of the rules, or 'patterned relations', that govern the way words combine to form phrases and phrases combine to form sentences.

xx Tom McArthur, The English Languages, Cambridge University Press 1998

xxi http://en.wikipedia.org/wiki/List_of_English-based_pidgins

xxii http://en.wikipedia.org/wiki/Creole_language

xxiii Mervyn Morris, (1993), Is English we speaking, English Today

xxiv http://nl.wikisource.org/wiki/Sinter_Mertes_veugelke

xxv http://www.trotsemoedern.nl/2008/11/heerijemeldoende sint maartenliedjes-2/

xxvi http://www.tigch.nl/dem/evenementen/2013/sintmaarten/sintmaartenlie djes.htm

xxvii http://www.phrases.org.uk/meanings/233450.html